The Play of Herod

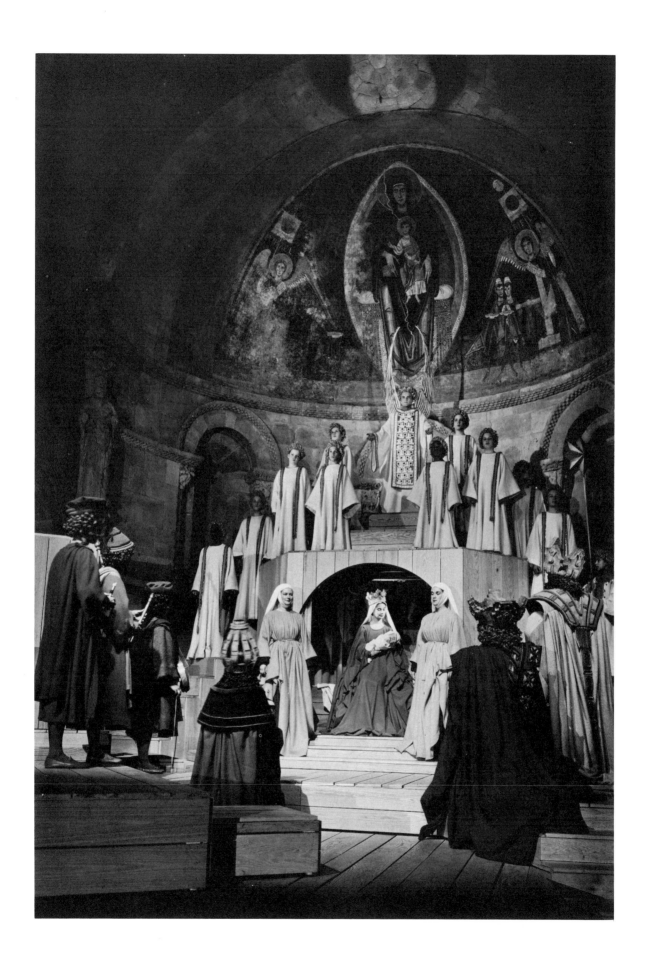

The Play of
HEROD

A Twelfth-Century Musical Drama

EDITED BY
NOAH GREENBERG

AND
WILLIAM L. SMOLDON

Transcribed into modern musical notation
and translated into English by William L. Smoldon;
edited for modern performance by Noah Greenberg

New York   OXFORD UNIVERSITY PRESS   1965

Contents

Acknowledgments

The editors gratefully acknowledge the advice and suggestions of Dr. Gustave Reese, Dom Anselm Hughes, The Benedictine Abbey of Solesmes, The Rev. James Kennedy O.S.C., Professor Jean Misrahi, and Charles C. Brown. They are especially thankful to Miss Margaret B. Freeman and The Cloisters staff who acted as artistic advisers to the original production. The editorial preparation and staging of *The Play of Herod* were aided by a grant from the Ford Foundation.

The frontispiece and other illustrative photographs are from the production of *The Play of Herod* as presented at The Cloisters, The Metropolitan Museum of Art, and are reproduced by kind permission of the Museum authorities.

The opening processional, "Orientis partibus", with the translation by Henry Copley Greene, is reprinted, by permission, from *Speculum*, VI, 4 (October 1931), published by the Mediaeval Academy of America.

The Play of Herod has been recorded by the New York Pro Musica and is available in the U.S.A. on Decca Records DXA 187 (Stereo DXSA 7187).

England: Brunswick Records
Australia: Decca Records

Text of the "Fleury play-book" (MS 201 of the Bibl. de Ville, Orléans) reproduced by kind permission of M. Claude Lannette, Conservateur aux Archives du Loiret.

Oxford University Press expresses its thanks to Messrs. Stainer and Bell of London, who published in 1960 an edition of *The Play of Herod*, also edited by W. L. Smoldon, and who have kindly assented to the publication of the present version.

Introduction to the Performing Edition

THE New York Pro Musica production of *The Play of Herod* was given its first performance at The Cloisters, The Metropolitan Museum of Art, in New York City in December 1963. The work in its present form (and this edition follows our performance as closely as possible) consists of two plays, *The Representation of Herod* and *The Slaying of the Children*, both from the twelfth-century French manuscript known as the "Fleury play-book." These works were written to appeal to a popular audience and were originally performed by the men and boys of the choir school attached to the monastic church of Fleury.

In our performance we added five musicians not mentioned in the manuscript: a percussionist, for the court of Herod, playing a tenor drum; a musician to Mary, who plays a bell carillon; and, for the Three Kings, three instrumentalists, who play a sopranino recorder, a tenor vielle, and a small bagpipe. Since the edition here is intended for practical use, we have substituted an oboe for the bagpipe and a modern viola for the tenor vielle. In addition to the music which appears in the manuscript we have interpolated an early processional song, the "Orientis partibus," two thirteenth-century French *estampies*, and, for the two crèche scenes, the thirteenth-century three-part motet, "Alleluya psallite." The plays were presented without an intermission and the running time is approximately one hour and fifteen minutes.

Inevitably one compares *The Play of Herod*

with *The Play of Daniel*, since they are both French medieval works dating from roughly the same period, but one is struck by the great differences between them rather than the similarities. Dramatically and musically *Daniel* appears as a colorful processional drama in which all the players are brought to and from the staging area with joyous, dance-like, and sometimes forceful, processional music. The central hero figure of Daniel binds the different scenes together, and both his interpretation of the handwriting on the wall and the immensely moving lament sung in the lions' den stand in bold contrast to the rest of the piece. In *Herod*, however, we are given a series of highly contrasting scenes, each developing its own mood—the gentle naïveté of the exchange between the Midwives and Shepherds; the joyousness of the Three Kings; the dark character of the Herod court; the simple happiness of the adoration of the Magi. Then in even greater contrast the shocking slaying of the Innocents, followed by the long, almost resigned, lament of Rachel and her Consolers. Both works call for the singing of the Te Deum and it is interesting to compare the sound of the Te Deum after each. At the end of *Daniel* the Te Deum seems to sound like a song of celebration for the triumph of good over evil, but following the slaying of the children the Te Deum comes as balm and brings with it great relief from tragedy.

The Play of Herod does contain a few dance-like processional pieces (numbers 15 and 47, for example), and these are quite appropriately assigned to the Magi, but much of the music consists of fragments of chant for "recitative," and it borrows a large number of older liturgical antiphons which appear throughout. These pieces must have been very well known in the twelfth century because the original manuscript gives only the openings ("incipits") of these religious songs.

The stage director for the New York Pro Musica production, Nikos Psacharopoulos, and the designer, Rouben Ter-Arutunian, arranged the stage area in the chancel in such a way that the court of Herod occupied stage right. This area was dominated by a raised throne and a long platform running diagonally toward down-stage center. The Manger occupied up-stage center and was much higher than the throne.

Encircling the sides and back of the Manger was a set of steps built for the Angel Choir, and the Archangel appeared on a platform above the Manger. The down-stage left area was reserved for the Shepherds in the field and the appearances in the chancel of the Three Kings. The slaying of the Innocents and the lament of Rachel were staged in the front center area.

It is extremely fortunate that many of the liturgical dramas that have survived contain a great number of stage instructions, and I think it is important that the stage director be as faithful to these rubrics as the musical director should be with the notation. The rubrics in *Herod* were an enormous help in preparing the play, telling us much about the medieval performance, the attitudes of the actors, the costuming, and the general spirit of the play. References like the "joyful" singing of the Innocents on their first appearance even give us clues about the interpretation of the music.

There is, of course, no *one* way to present a work such as *Herod*. The New York Pro Musica Cloisters performance should not be thought of as a definitive presentation, but rather as one possible approach.

The present edition attempts to reconstruct the 1963 performance, making certain concessions to practicality. The Shepherds in the Cloisters performances were sung by countertenors (male altos). These roles could easily be performed by female altos and are so assigned here. I have already listed the substitution of modern for old instruments above. The original stage instructions are printed, in literal translation, throughout, and additional suggestions for staging appear in italics. The suggested repetitions of certain sections, which we found necessary for our own production, are of course optional, as are the interpolated sections.

The doubling of certain roles is suggested here, but this depends entirely on the number of performers available. Only two very fast costume changes are involved: the Angel Choir becoming the Innocents and the Second King changing into Joseph. The other suggested doublings are the Midwives and Shepherds changing into Mothers-Consolers; and the First and Third Kings, Scribes, and Courtiers becoming Soldiers for the slaying scene. However, if the director has a large number of players at his disposal, doubling becomes unnecessary.

It is also possible to combine certain roles. Aside from the Angel Choir, the manuscript refers to a number of Angels, but in our performance we found it more practical to use an Archangel, who remains at his station above the Manger throughout the entire play. Although it is not absolutely clear, the manuscript seems to call for Spokesmen (or Interpreters) as well as two young Courtiers "dressed as young men" in the Herod court, but these are very small parts indeed and we combined the roles of Courtier and Spokesmen. For school productions it might be useful to have different children play the roles of Angels and Holy Innocents. Apparently, both Mothers of the Innocents and Consolers to Rachel were used in the twelfth-century production, but here again we found it more practical to combine these roles. Thus in *The Slaying of the Children* at number 13, the Mothers of the Children come on to intercede with the slayers and during the lament of Rachel these Mothers become Rachel's Consolers. Again, many directors might prefer not to combine these roles.

The bell carillon, played by the Musician to Mary, has an extremely important role in our production. In some of the processional pieces, the bells were used as hand-bells, but through most of the play they were mounted on a specially constructed wooden rack and hung in sequence so that they could give pitches to the performers and accompany a good deal of the singing. The bells were struck with leather mallets and were hung in the following order:

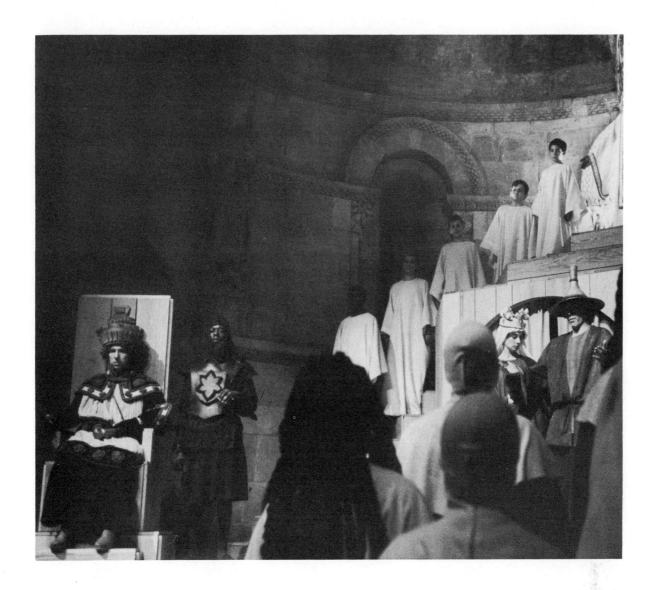

The only major stage properties are the curtained Manger with its surrounding steps for the Angel Choir, and Herod's throne, which stands on a platform extending from downstage right toward stage center. The smaller properties include:

a star mounted on a long pole

a medallion, again mounted on a pole, depicting the Lamb of God carrying a cross (an alternative to the medallion would be a banner)

swords for Herod, Archelaus, Armiger, and the Soldiers of the court

a scepter for Herod

a large book for the Scribes

staffs for the Shepherds

three gifts and three pillows for the Bearers of the Three Kings

a doll wrapped in swaddling clothes to represent the Christ-child

a coverlet for the Magi

As regards costuming, the basic guide should be the many medieval depictions of this very famous story. There are hundreds of such examples from twelfth- and thirteenth-century art which will serve better than any description.

NOAH GREENBERG

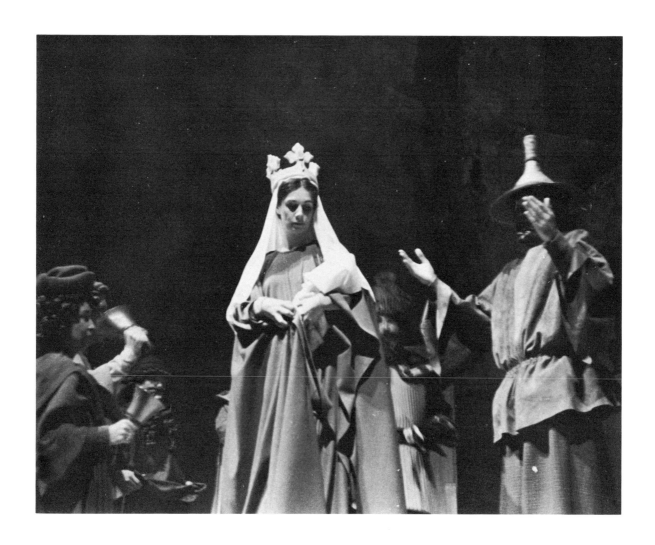

Summary of the Action

THE REPRESENTATION OF HEROD

"When Herod and the other persons are ready, an Angel shall appear with a multitude of the heavenly host. Seeing this, the shepherds are sore afraid. He shall announce salvation unto them, while the rest keep silent." Thus begins *The Play of Herod* according to the rubric in the "Fleury play-book." Then follows the journey of the shepherds to Bethlehem and their adoration of the Christ-child. The dialogue at the Manger is between the Shepherds and two Midwives, who, according to the apocryphal gospels, were present at the scene of the Nativity. After the Shepherds have worshipped the Child, they invite the audience to adore him also.

Meanwhile the Magi approach from three separate parts of the church as if they came from three different countries. The Magi greet each other, behold the Star, and proceed to Jerusalem, led by the Star.

At this point King Herod's court comes into action. Herod sends his armor-bearer (Armiger) and then his courtiers to inquire of the Magi who they are and what their purpose is. When the Magi are conducted to Herod they are again questioned, this time by Herod himself. The Magi explain that they have come from the East to seek a new-born King. Hearing this, Herod commands his Scribes "who are ready with their beards" to search in their books for a prophecy of such a King. The Scribes, turning over the pages for a long time, hand their book to Herod,

pointing with a finger to the prophecy. Herod is seized with fury, and throws down the book; but his son, Archelaus, "comes forward to appease his father." And so Herod sends forth the Magi to search for the new-born King and bids them return to him with news of the Child.

The Magi, again following the Star, proceed toward Bethlehem, and on the way they meet and converse with the Shepherds returning from the Manger. As was the case with the Shepherds, the Magi speak with the Midwives at the Manger, and then offer their gifts to the Child. This done, they fall asleep and are warned by the Angel in a dream to return home another way. The Magi depart, avoiding King Herod's court.

THE SLAYING OF THE CHILDREN

The Slaying of the Children begins with the entrance of the young boys, the Innocents, in white garments, who later follow the symbolic Lamb bearing a cross.

Meanwhile Herod ceremoniously receives his scepter from Armiger, his armor-bearer.

At this point the Angel warns Joseph to flee into Egypt, for Herod would seek the Child to destroy him. And so the Holy Family departs, Mary carrying her son.

Then Armiger announces to Herod that the Magi have journeyed home another way. This so angers Herod that he seizes his sword and is about to kill himself when Armiger suggests that he slay all the young boys instead, for perhaps "among them is found the Christ." So the Children are put to the sword while the Mothers try in vain to prevent the massacre. Rachel, one of the Mothers, sings a long lament while Consolers attempt to ease her sorrow. This scene is developed from the prophecy of Jeremiah quoted in the gospel of Matthew: "A voice in Rama was heard, lamentation and great mourning; Rachel bewailing her children, and would not be comforted, because they are not." After Rachel has been conducted from the scene, the Angel sings "Suffer the little children to come unto me"; and at the voice of the Angel, the Children "rise up and enter the choir singing."

Now Herod dies and his son Archelaus rules in his place.

In the final scene the Angel announces to Joseph that it is safe to "come out of Egypt" because Herod is dead, and the Holy Family returns into Galilee, Joseph singing "Gaude, gaude, gaude."

The cantor begins the Te Deum and the play ends.

MARGARET B. FREEMAN
THE CLOISTERS
METROPOLITAN MUSEUM OF ART
NEW YORK CITY

xiv

The Play of Herod

PERFORMING EDITION

Characters

Solo voices

Archangel	TENOR
Two Midwives	SOPRANOS
Three Magi	BARITONES
Armiger	BASS
Herod	BASS
Archelaus, Herod's Son	BASS
Two Courtiers	TENORS
Two Scribes	TENORS
Joseph	BARITONE
Rachel	MEZZO SOPRANO

Choir*

Angel Choir	TEN SOPRANOS
Three Shepherds	THREE ALTOS
Holy Innocents	TEN SOPRANOS
Soldiers	SIX BARITONES AND/OR TENORS
Mothers-Consolers	FIVE SOPRANOS AND/OR ALTOS

Instrumentalists

Musician to Mary	BELL CARILLON
Musicians to the Magi	SOPRANINO RECORDER
	VIOLA
	OBOE
Musician to Herod	TENOR DRUM

Actors

Virgin Mary	A YOUNG WOMAN
Star Bearer	A CHILD
Two Soldiers	TWO MEN
Three Gift Bearers	THREE CHILDREN

*The size of the choir may vary

The Representation of Herod

OPENING PROCESSIONAL

* *When Mary and the Child are ready behind the drawn curtains of the Manger and the Three Kings have taken their positions at the rear of the nave, the Archangel prepares to ascend the steps leading to his place above the Manger at the sound of the bells.*

The following members of the cast, in the order listed, enter from the rear of the nave and proceed down the center aisle singing "Orientis partibus."

Musician to Mary (Bells g¹ and d¹), Star Bearer, Angel Choir, Midwives, Shepherds, Courtiers, Scribes, Herod, Archelaus, Armiger

1. O - ri - en - tis par - ti - bus   Ad - ven - ta - vit a - si - nus,
    Out from the lands of Orient   Was the Ass divinely sent

2. Hic in col - li - bus Si - chan   Iam nu - tri - tus sub Ru - ben,
    In the hills of Sichem bred,   Under Reuben nourished,

3. Sal - tu vin - cit hin - nu - los,   Dam - mas et cap - re - o - los,
    Higher leap'd than goats can bound,   Doe and roebuck circled round;

4. Au - rum de A - ra - bi - a,   Thus et myr - rham de Sa - ba
    Red gold from Arabia,   Frankincense and from Sheba

5. Dum tra - hit ve - hi - cu - la,   Mul - ta cum sar - cin - u - la
    While he drags long carriages,   Loaded down with baggages,

6. Cum a - ris - tis or - de - um   Co - me - dit et car - du - um:
    Chews the ears with barleycorn   Thistledown with thistlecorn.

7. A - men di - cas, a - si - ne,   Iam sa - tur de gra - mi - ne
    Stuff'd with grass, yet speak and say   Amen, ass, with ev'ry bray:

Stage directions appearing as rubrics in the original manuscript are printed in roman. Editorial additions are printed in italic.

1. Pul - cher et for - tis - si - mus,
   Strong and very fair was he,
   Sar - ci - nis ap - tis - si - mus.
   Bearing burdens gallantly.

2. Tran - si - it per Ior - da - nem,.
   Jordan's stream he traversed,
   Sa - li - it in Beth - le - em.
   Into Bethlehem he sped.

3. Su - per dro - me - da - ri - os
   Median dromedaries' speed,
   Ve - lox Ma - di - a - ne - os.
   Overcame and took the lead.

4. Tu - lit in ec - cle - si - a
   Myrrh he brought and, through the door,
   Vir - tus A - si - na - ri - a.
   Into the church he bravely bore.

5. Il - li - us man - di - bu - la
   He, with jaws insatiate,
   Du - ra - te - rit pa - bu - la
   Fodder hard doth masticate.

6. Tri - ti - cum e pa - le - a
   On the threshing floor his feet
   Se - gre - gat in a - re - a
   Separate the chaff from wheat.

7. A - men, A - men, i - te - ra,
   Amen; Amen, say again;
   As - per - na - re ve - te - ra
   Ancient sins hold in disdain.

1.-7. Hez, sir as - ne, hez!
Heigh, Sir Ass, oh heigh!

(If the length of the nave requires it, some of the verses may be repeated.)

At the conclusion of the procession, the Angel Choir has taken its place above the Manger and the Star Bearer stands to one side near the Angels. The Midwives station themselves at the foot of the Manger and the Shepherds occupy down-stage left. Herod and his court briefly take their places and then leave by up-stage right before the end of the processional.

SCENE I ANGELS AND SHEPHERDS

At the sound of the bell preceding "Nolite timere vos," the Shepherds turn with fear, looking up to the Archangel.

Here begins the Book of the Representation, "Herod." Herod and the other members of the cast being ready to go on, then let the Angel appear above with a multitude of other Angels. Seeing this, the Shepherds are afraid. While the other Angels still remain silent, let the Angels sing greetings:

1 Moderately fast

BELLS

ARCHANGEL

Nó - li - te ___ ti - mé - re ___ vos!
Be no more affrighted!

ec - ce ___ e - nim e - van - ge - lí - zo vo - bis
For behold, I bring you good tidings

gáu - di - um mag - num quod e - rit o - mni ___ pó - pu - lo;
of great joy which shall be to all people;

qui - a na - tus ___ est no - bis hó - di - e
for unto us is born this day in the city of David

Sal - vá - tor mun - di in ci - vi - tá - te
a Saviour of the world,

Da - vid, ___ et ___ hoc ___ vo - bis ___ si - gnum:
and this shall be a sign:

In - ve - ni - é - tis in - fán - tem pan - nis ___
Ye shall find the babe wrapped in swaddling

in - vo - lú - tum et ___ pó - si - tum ___ in ___ prae - sé - pi - o
clothes lying in a manger

in ___ me - di - o du - um ___ a - ni - ma - li - um. ___
between two beasts.

5

The Shepherds, facing the Angels, fall to their knees.
And suddenly let all the multitude with the Angel say;

2   **Joyous and very bright**

BELLS

ANGEL CHOIR

ƒ

Glo - ri - a in ex - cél - sis De - o! ___
Glory to God in the highest,

et in ter - ra ___ pax ho - mi - ni - bus bo - nae
and on earth peace, good will towards men;

vo - lun - tá - tis; al - le - lú - ia, al - le - lú - ia!

Then let the Shepherds, arising, sing to each other:

3   **Timidly**

p

SHEPHERDS

Tran - se - á - mus ___ us - que ___ Béth - le - em,
Let us now go unto Bethlehem,

et ___ vi - de - á - mus ___ hoc ___ ver - bum quod fac - tum ___ est,
and see this thing which is come to pass,

quod ___ fe - cit Dó - mi - nus et ___ os - tén - dit ___ no - bis.
which the Lord has done and made known unto us.

And thus let them proceed as far as the Manger which has been prepared
at the monastery doors, and then let two women guarding the Manger
question the Shepherds, saying:

4

BELLS

Gently

MIDWIVES

p

Quem _ quáe - ri - tis, pás - to - res, dí - ci - te? _____
Whom do you seek,   O shepherds?   Say to us.

Let the Shepherds reply:

5

SHEPHERDS

Sal - va - tó - rem _ Chri - stum Dó - - mi - num;
The Saviour, Jesus Christ, the Lord;

In - fán - tem _ pan - nis in - vo - lú - tum,
The infant wrapped in swaddling clothes,

se - cún - dum sér - mo - nem _ an - gé - li - cum.
according to the words of the angel.

The women:

6

BELLS

Boldly

1st MIDWIFE

mf

A - dest hic _____ pár - vu - lus
Behold!   Here with Mary his mother is the little child,

cum Ma - ri - a _____ ma - tre _____ e - ius,

2nd MIDWIFE

de qua _ du - dum _ va - ti - ci - nán - do
whose coming the prophet Isaiah in days long ago did foretell, saying:

Y - sa - í - as pro - phé - ta ___ dí - xe - rat:

BOTH MIDWIVES

"Ec - ce ___ vir - go ___ con - cí - pi - et
"Behold, a virgin shall conceive

et pá - ri - et fí - li - um!"
and shall bear a son!"

The Midwives slowly open the curtains of the Manger, showing Mary and the Child, and then close them at the end of the following motet.

6a **Delicately in moderate tempo**

1st MIDWIFE

Al - le, psal - li - te cum lu - ya,
Sing "Alle-" with "-luya"!

2nd MIDWIFE

Al, ___ Al - le
Sing "Alle-"

ARCHANGEL

Al - le - lu - ya, al - le -

[a] ___ Al - le, ___ con - cre - pan - do psal - li - te cum
Sing vigorously, "Alleluia"!

psal - li - te cum lu - ya, [a] ___
with "-luya"!

- lu - ya, al - le - lu -

lu - ya, [a]

Al - le, __ con - cre -pan - do psal - li - te cum lu - -
Sing vigorously, "Alleluia"!

ya, al - - le - - lu - ya.

Al - le, __ cor - de vo - to De - o to - to psal - li - te cum
Sing to God with all your heart, "Alleluia"!

ya, [a]

al - - - le - - lu -

lu - ya, [a]

Al - le, __ cor - de vo - to De - o to - to psal - li - te cum
Sing to God with all your heart, "Alleluia"!

ya, al - - - le - - lu -

__ al - le - lu - - ya!

lu - - ya, al - le - lu - ya!

ya, al - le - lu - - ya.

9

Then let the Shepherds, prostrating themselves, adore the Child saying:

Then rising, let them invite the people around to worship the Infant,
saying to the crowd near by:

The Shepherds retire to up-stage left.

8b

BELLS

ANGEL CHOIR

Glo - ri - a in ex-cél - sis De - o! ___
Glory to God in the highest,

et in ter - ra ___ pax ho - mi - ni - bus bo - nae
and on earth peace, good will towards men;

vo - lun - tá - tis; al - le - lú - ia, al - le - lú - ia!

The Three Kings, each with Musician and Gift Bearer, stand ready at the rear of the nave as follows:

Right Aisle—1st King with Recorder Player and Gift Bearer
Center Aisle—2nd King with Oboe Player and Gift Bearer
Left Aisle—3rd King with Viola Player and Gift Bearer

Musicians began their estampie while walking a few steps into the nave, returning to follow their Kings when they begin to sing. The Magi procession should be timed so that the Three Kings meet on the steps leading to the center of the stage or chancel.

8c

RECORDER

RECORDER
OBOE VIOLA

RECORDER

ALL

SCENE II   THE THREE KINGS

Meanwhile, let the Magi advance, each coming from his own corner as
if from his own region, meeting before the altar, or at the place of the
Star, and while they are approaching, let the 1st say:

9¹ **With dignity in moderately fast tempo**

1st KING

Stel - la ful - gó - re ní - mi - o rú - ti - lat!
With an exceeding brightness this star doth blaze!

9²

2nd KING

Quem ven - tú - rum o - lim pro - phé - ta si - gná - ve - rat.
Of whose advent prophets have spoken in ancient days.

Then standing side by side, let him on the right hand say to the one in the middle:

10¹

And let the other reply:

10²

(Accompanying the Kiss of Peace)

10a

Then let them kiss each other thus:

The middle to the left and the left to the right—a salutation to each one
(therefore it would seem the middle to the right also). **Then let them in-**
dicate the Star to each other.

11¹ 2nd KING
Ec - ce Stel - la!
See, the Star!

11² 1st KING
Ec - ce Stel - la!
See, the Star!

11³ 3rd KING
Ec - ce Stel - la! ____
See, the Star!

*As the Kings kiss and then sing "Ecce Stella," the three Musicians stand
to one side and the three Bearers to the other.*

The Kings, Bearers, and Musicians are slowly led to down-stage left.
The Star then advancing and leading them, let them follow saying:

12 **Quickly**
mf
3 KINGS
E - á - mus er - go et in - qui - rá - mus e - um
Accordingly, let us now hasten to seek him,

of - fe - rén - tes ____ e - i mu - ne - ra. ____
unto him offering precious gifts.

Held back
1st KING   2nd KING   3rd KING
Au - rum ____ thus; ____ et __ myr - rham.
Here is gold;   frankincense;   and myrrh.

With motion
3 KINGS
Qui - a __ scri - ptum __ di - dí - ci - mus; "A - do - rá - bunt e - um o -
For these words are known unto us: "All the Kings shall offer him worship;

mnes re - - ges; o - mnes gen-tes sér-vi-ent e - i."
all people shall give to him service."

Coming to the choir door, let them question those standing by:

13 **Deliberately**

3 KINGS

Dí - ci - te no - bis, O —— Je -ró -so -li - mi -tá -
Make known unto us, O ye citizens of Jerusalem;

ni — ci - ves; u - bi est — ex-pec-tá-ti - o gén - ti - um?
where now is he, expected of the people?

U - bi — est qui na-tus est rex Ju-de-o - rum, quem si -gnis ce -lés -
Where now is he who is born the King of the Jews, whom, revealed by wondrous

ti - bus — á - gni - tum vé -'- ni -mus a - do -rá - re?
signs from heaven, we have come here to adore?

While the estampie is being played Herod enters with Archelaus, the
Armiger, his Musician, two Courtiers, and two Soldiers. They all take
their places in the throne area.

13a **Brightly (in one)**

RECORDER

ALL

RECORDER

ALL

VIOLA

SCENE III HEROD'S COURT

Having seen them, let Herod send the Armiger to them, who says:

14 **Forcefully**

ARMIGER

Quae __ re - rum __ nó - vi - tas, aut quae __ cau - sa
What unwonted events, *or what reason moved you thus to attempt an*

su - bé - git __ vos i - gnó - tas temp - tá - re; __ vi - as?
unknown journey?

Quo tén - di - tis __ er - go? Quod ge - nus? Un - de __
Where, then, are you going? *What race are you?* *Where is your home?*

do - mo? Pa - cem ne huc fer - tis an __ ar - ma?
Which do you bring to us, peace or war?

The reply of the Magi:

15 **With joyous dignity, moderately fast**

3 KINGS

Cál - de - i __ su - mus; pa - -
We are Chaldaeans; *bearers of peace we are;*

RECORDER
OBOE

VIOLA

cem __ fé - ri - mus; Re - gem re - gum quáe - ri -
Seek we here the King of kings

mus, quem na - tum es - se stel - la in - di - cat, quae
Whose birth is now revealed by the Star,
quae

fúl - - go - re _ cé - te - ris clá - ri - or _
shining of which has exceeded all others in brightness.

rú - - ti - - lat. _

The Armiger returns and salutes the King:
On bended knee let him say:

16

ARMIGER

Vi - vat Rex in ae - tér - num! _
Live for ever, O King!

18

17

HEROD

Sal - vet te grá - ti - a me - a! _____
Greetings to you and our thanks!

Armiger to the King:

18

ARMIGER

Ad - - sunt ____ no - bis Dó - mi - ne tres ____
O lord and master, there are three strangers among us,

ví - ri ____ i - gno - ti, ab o - ri - én - te
who have journeyed from far Eastern lands;

ve - ni - én - tes; nó - vi - ter ____ na - tum
seeking to find a certain King who is newly born.

quem - - dam re - gem quae. - ri - tán - tes.

Then let Herod send his Spokesmen or Interpreters *(Courtiers)* to the
Magi, saying:

19 **Nervously**

DRUM

HEROD

Lae - ti ín - qui - si - tó - res, qui ____ sunt ____
My fluent ambassadors, discover who these Kings may be;

in - qúi - ri - te ____ re - ges; af - fó - re quos nos - tris
question them concerning whom rumour is

iam fa - ma re - vól - vit ___ in ___ o - ris.
already abroad.

*While beckoning and leading the Courtiers to the Magi the Armiger
sings:*

19a

ARMIGER

Lae - ti ín - qui - si - tó - res, qui ___ sunt ___
My fluent ambassadors, discover who these Kings may be;

in - qúi - ri - te ___ re - ges; af - fó - re quos nos - tris
question them concerning whom rumour is already

iam fa - ma re - vól - vit ___ . in ___ o - ris.
abroad.

The Interpreters *(Courtiers)* to the Magi:

20

2 COURTIERS

Prín - ci - pis e - dic - tu, re - ges, pre - sci - re vé - ni - mus quo ___
Sent to you by our lord's command, we are here, O Kings, to find why you

sit pro - féc - tus hic ves' - ter, et un - de pro - féc - tus.
have journeyed hither, and also whence you come.

The Magi:

21

3 KINGS

Re - gem qúae - si - tum du - ce stel - la ___
Led by a Star we are seeking the King who is promised;

sí - gni - fi - cá - tum; mú - ne - re pro - ví - so
provided with gifts we hasten to offer our adoration.

pro - pe - rá - mus e - um — ve - ne - - ran - do.

The Spokesmen *(Courtiers)* returning to Herod:

22

2 COURTIERS

Re - ges — sunt — Á - ra - bum; cum tri - no —
Kings of Araby are they; bringing a threefold gift;

mú - - ne - re; — Na - tum quae - - runt
seeking a new-born infant,

in - fán - - tem, quem — mon - strant sí - de - ra re - gem.
whom the stars proclaim to be King.

The Armiger to Herod:

22a

ARMIGER

Re - ges — sunt — Á - ra - bum; cum tri - no —
Kings of Araby are they; bringing a threefold gift;

mú - - ne - re; — Na - tum quae - - runt
seeking a new-born infant,

in - fán - - tem, quem — mon - strant sí - de - ra re - gem.
whom the stars proclaim to be King.

Herod, sending the Armiger to bring the Magi:

23

DRUM

HEROD

An - - te ve - ní - re — iu - be,
Order them to attend us,

quo pos - sim sín - gu - la _ sci - re   qui sunt; _____
that we may learn each of these things;   who they are;

cur _____ vé - ni - ant;   quo _____ nos
whence they have come;   what rumour has brought them to us?

ru - mó - - - re _ re - quí - rant?

Armiger:

24

ARMIGER

Quod man-das, cí - ti - us,   Rex in - cli - te, _____   per - fi - ci - é - tur.
What you have commanded,   O famous King,   swiftly shall be done.

The Armiger returns to the Magi while the court sings.

24a

2 COURTIERS

Quod man-das, cí - ti - us,   Rex in - cli - te, _____   per - fi - ci - é - tur.
What you have commanded,   O famous King,   swiftly shall be done.

The Armiger to the Magi:

25   **Forcefully**

ARMIGER   *f*

Ré - gi - a vos man - dá - ta _____ vo - cant; non sé - gni - ter _ i - te!
You are summoned by the King's command;   Come now without delay!

The Armiger, leading the Magi to Herod:

26 **Broadly** *f*

ARMIGER

En __ Ma - gi __ vé - ni - unt! Et __ re - gem __
Behold, the Magi come!   And led by a star, they seek a King, newly

VIOLA

f

na - tum stel - la _____ du - ce, re - qúi - runt.
born.

26a

RECORDER
OBOE

VIOLA

Herod to the Magi:

27   **With arrogance**

HEROD

Quae _ sit _____ cau - sa _ vi - ae?
Why make you this journey?

Qui _ vos?
Who are you?

Vel _ un - de _ ve - ni' - tis?
From what land have you come?

Di' - ci - te!
Answer us!

The Magi:

28   **Calmly**

mp

3 KINGS

Rex _ est _____ cau - sa _ vi - ae;
The reason is a King;

Re - ges _____
Kings are we, come from

su _ - mus ex _ A - rá - bi - tis, huc _____ ve - ni - én - tes.
Arabia, journeying hither.

Quáe - ri - mus en _ re - gem re - gnán - ti - bus im - pe - ri - tán - tem;
Behold, we are seeking a king who rules all other rulers;

Quem na - tum _ mun - do lac - tat Ju - dá - i - ca vir - - - go.
who, newly born, is suckled by a Jewish virgin.

24

Herod to the Magi:

29

Re - gem, quem quǽ - ri - tis,
By what sign did you learn that the king whom you are seeking had been born?

na - tum es - se quo si - gno di - di - cís - tis?

The Magi:

30

Il - lum na - tum __ es - se di - dí - ci - mus
In our own Eastern lands we had learned that He was indeed born;

in O - ri - én - te; Stel - la - mon - strán - te.
this the Star showed us.

Herod:

31

Si __ il - lum re - gná - re __ cré -
Do you believe that he indeed reigns?

di - tis? _____ Dí - ci - te no - bis!
Say unto us!

The Magi:

32

3 KINGS

Il - lum ___ re - gná - re fa - tén - tes, cum mý - sti - cis
Proclaiming that he indeed reigns, and bearing with us sacred gifts,

mu - né - ri - bus, de ter - - ra ___ lon - gín - qua a - do -
from distant lands have we come ready to worship him;

rá - re ___ vé - - ni - mus; tri - num De - um
With three gifts paying reverence to the one

ve - ne - rán - tes tri - bus ___ cum mu - né - ri - bus. _____
God that is three.

Then let them display the gifts. Let the First say:

33 **Slowly**

1st KING

Au - ro re - gem. _____
Gold for a king.

2nd KING

Thu - re De - - um.
Incense for a God.

3rd KING

Myr - rha ___ mor - tá - lem.
Myrrh for a mortal.

Then let Herod command the Courtiers, who are seated with him dressed
as young men, to bring the Scribes, who, bearded, are near at hand:

The Courtiers to the Scribes, who are bringing with them the Books of
the Prophets:

Then let Herod question the Scribes, saying:

dí - ci - te si quid de hoc pu - e - ro scri -
if you see anything written in the book concerning this boy.

ptum — vi - dé - ri - tis in li - bro.

Then let two Scribes turn the pages, and finally, as if having discovered
the prophecy, let them say:

37 **Slow**

2 SCRIBES

Ví - di - mus, — Dó - mi - ne, in pro - phe - tá - rum — lí - ne - is;
We see, O Sire, in the lines that the Prophets have written:

na - sci — Chri - stum in — Béth - le - em — Ju - dae, — ci - vi - tá - te
"Christ is born in Bethlehem in Judea, in the City of David."

Da - vid; pro - phé - ta sic — va - ti - ci - nán - te.
This is what the prophet has foretold.

And indicating with a finger let them pass the Book to the incredulous
King:

38 **Even slower**

2 SCRIBES

mf

"Beth - le - em non es — mí - ni - ma
"Thou, Bethlehem, art not the least

in — prin - ci - pí - bus — Ju - - - da;
among the princes of Judah;

ex te e - nim éx - i - et — dux
for out of thee shall come a governor

38a

2 COURTIERS

2 SCRIBES

Then let Herod, having seen the prophecy and inflamed with fury, throw down the Book: but let his Son *(Archelaus)*, hearing the tumult, come forward to pacify his Father and stand there to greet him:

39 **In anger—moderately fast**

Herod:

40

ae ___ Tu - o gé - rens _____ nó - mi - ne!
manifested in thy name!

ARCHELAUS
AND HEROD

Rex est ___ na - tus ___ fór - ti - - or, No - bis ___
Yet we hear of a greater still, who as a kingly babe

et po - tén - ti - or. Vé - re - or ne ___ só - li -
is born. Truly there is fear that we

o ___ Nos ex - trá - het _____ ré - gi - o!
may from our royal throne be torn!

Then let the Son, speaking slightingly of Christ, offer himself as a defender saying:

41

DRUM

ARCHELAUS

Con - tra ___ il - lum ___ ré - gu - lum, Con - tra ___
'Gainst that king of little worth, 'gainst the babe, new

na - tum ___ pár - vu - lum, Iu - be, ___ pá - ter, ___ fí - li -
brought to birth, Give word, father, to thy son,

um   Hoc in - í - re _____ proe - li – um!
that this war be now begun.

ARCHELAUS
AND HEROD

Rex est ____ na - tus ___ fór - ti – or,   No - bis __
Yet we hear of a greater still,   who as a kingly babe

et po - tén - ti – or.   Vé - re – or ne __ só - li -
is born.   Truly there is fear that we

o __   Nos ex - trá - het _____ ré - gi – o!
may from our royal throne be torn!

Then at last let Herod send away the Magi that they may search for the
Child, after vowing homage before them to the new-born King, saying:

42   **Falsely**
      mp

HEROD

I – – - te,   et de pú - e - ro di - li - gén – - ter
Go forth,   and with the utmost diligence make search for the new-born child;

in - ves - ti - gá – - te;   et in - vén - to,
and finding him,

re - de - ún - tes ___ mi - hi re - nun - ci - á – te,
return to us again bringing word of him,

ut et e - go vé - ni - ens a - dó – rem ___ e - um.
so that we also may come to offer homage.

32

42a

As the Magi are going out, let the Star, which has not yet been perceived by Herod, go on before them. Let them point it out to each other as they go. After seeing it, let Herod and his Son threaten it with their swords:

As they play, the Kings, their Musicians and Bearers leave the court and move to down-stage left. Herod's court leaves from up-stage right.

42b **Playfully and fast (in one)**

34

SCENE IV ADORATION OF THE MAGI

Magi:

43

3 KINGS

Ec - ce _ Stel - la in o - ri - én - te _ prae - ví - da,
Lo! The Star   in the East already espied,

I - te - rum prae - cé - dit nos lú - ci - da! _____
Shining brightly,, still doth remain our guide!

Meanwhile let the Shepherds returning from the Manger come along
with rejoicing and singing:

44

SHEPHERDS

O _____ re - gem _ cae - - - li, _____
O, King of Heaven,

Add Angel Choir

SHEPHERDS AND
ANGEL CHOIR

cu - i _ tá - li - a _____ fa - mu - lán -
to whom service is given in all obedience.

tur _____ ob - - sé - qui - a! _____

Stá - bu - lo _____ pó - ni - tur _____
He who unites the world is laid in a stable;

qui cón - ti - net _____ mun - - dum; _____

ia - cet in _ prae - sé - pi - o, _____
he is lying in a manger

et in nú - bi - bus _____ to - nat. ___
and yet thunders in the clouds!

To whom the Magi:

45 **Slowly**
p

3 KINGS

Quem vi - dís - tis? _____
Whom have you seen?

As they sing the following song, the Shepherds walk into the nave and up the center aisle. If the length of the nave requires it,.let them repeat No. 46 until they disappear.

Shepherds:

46 **Innocently**
p

SHEPHERDS

Se - cún - dum _____ quod __ di - ctum
In accordance   with what was told to us by the Angel

est no - bis ab An - ge - lo ___ de pú - e - ro i - sto, ___
                                                    concerning this Child,

in - vé - ni - mus ín - fan - tem pan - nis in - vo - lú - tum,
we found the new-born infant   wrapped in swaddling clothes,

Et __ pó - si - tum ___ in ___ prae - sé - pi - o ___
and lying in a manger

in __ mé - di - o du - um ___ a - ni - má - li - um. ___
between two animals.

After the Shepherds have gone, let the Magi follow the Star as far as
the Manger singing:

47   **Joyously**

37

De vir-gi-ne-o na-tus ú-te-ro; pó-ni-tur in prae-sé-pi-o
Has been born of a Virgin Mother; in a lowly manger laid.

Ser-mo cé-ci-nit quem va-tí-di-cus stant si-mul
Sharing shelter with an ox and ass even as prophecies had said.

bos - et á - si - nus. ____ Sed o - rí - tur stel - la
But the shining star arises rendering its homage to the

lú - ci - da, prae - bi - tú - ra Dó - mi - no ob - sé - qui - a,
Lord,

Quem Bá - la - am ex Ju - dá - í - ca na - sci - tú - rum
Destined to be born of Jewish stock, even thus did Balaam speak prophetic word.

dí - xe - rat pro - sá - pi - a. Haec no - stró - rum o - cu -
This, the brilliance of the Star, by its dazzling light has

40

los ful - gu - rán - ti lú - mi - ne prae-strin - xit lú - ci - da,
blinded our eyes;

Et nos ip - sos pro - vi - de du - cens ad — cu - ná - bu -
Also, providentially, by its splendour leading us to where the cradle lies!

lam re - splen - dens ___ fúl - gi - da! _____

Then let the Midwives, seeing the Magi, say to each other:

48

Gently

mp

MIDWIVES

Qui sunt ___ hi - i qui, _____ stel - la ___ du - ce, _____
Who are these who, led by a star,

nos ___ a - de - un - tes in - au - dí - ta fe - runt? _____
advance towards us carrying strange burdens?

The Magi:

49

3 KINGS

Nos su - mus ___ quos ___ cér - ni - tis, re - ges Thar - sis,
We whom you see here are the Kings of Tarsus,

et Á - ra - bum, et Sa - ba, ___ do - na fe - rén - tes ___
and Araby, and Saba, bearing their gifts to the new-born Christ,

Chri - - sto na - to, ___ Re - gi, Dó - mi - no,
the King, the Lord,

quem, stel - la — du - ·cén - te, a - do - rá - re ʼvé - ni — mus.
whom, guided by the Star, we are coming to adore.

The Midwives, showing the Boy:

50 **Stronger**

MIDWIVES

Ec - ce! pu - er a - dest quem qúae - ri - tis. Iam pro - pe - rá - te et
Behold! here is the Child whom you have sought. Now hasten to offer adoration!

a - do - rá - te, qui - a ip - se — est re - dém - pti - o — mun - di! ____
for he is truly the Saviour of the world!

The Midwives slowly open the Manger curtain and close it at the end
of the motet.

50a

1st MIDWIFE
5 ANGELS

Al - le, psal - li - te cum lu - - ya,
Sing "Alle-" with "-luya"!

2nd MIDWIFE
5 ANGELS

Al, _____ Al - le
Sing "Alle-"

ARCHANGEL

Al - le - - lu - ya, al - le -

[a] _____ Al - le, — con - cre - pan - do psal - li - te cum
Sing vigorously, "Alleluia"!

psal - li - te cum lu - ya, [a] _____
with "-luya"!

- lu - ya, al - - le - lu -

lu - ya,   [a] _____

—   Al - le, __ con - cre - pan - do psal - li - te cum lu - __
Sing vigorously, "Alleluia"!

ya,   al - - - le - - lu - ya.

Al - le, __ cor - de vo - to De - o to - to psal - li - te
Sing to God with all your heart, "Alleluia"!

ya,   [a] _____

al - - - le - - lu -

lu - ya,   [a] _____

—   Al - le, __ cor - de vo - to De - o to - to psal - li - te cum
Sing to God with all your heart, "Alleluia"!

ya,   al - - - le - - lu -

—   al - le - lu - - ya!

lu - - ya, al - le - lu - ya!

ya,   al - le - lu - - ya.

The Magi:

51 **Broadly**

BELLS

3 KINGS

p 1 KING

Sal - ve, Rex sae - cu - ló - rum! _____
All hail, King of the Ages!

2 KINGS

Sal - ve De - us de - ó - rum! _____
All hail, God above all gods!

3 KINGS

Sal - ve, Sa - lus mor - tu - ó - rum! _____
All hail, Saviour of the dead!

Then let the Magi, prostrating themselves, adore the Boy and make
their offerings. The First will say:

52

1st KING

p

Sús - ci - pe, _____ Rex, _____ au - rum,
Accept, O King, gold,

Re - gis _____ si - gnum.
emblem of a King.

The Second:

3rd KING

Sús - ci - pe _____ myr - rham, si -
Accept myrrh, emblem of burial.

gnum ___ se - pul - tú - re

The Third:

2nd KING

Sús - ci - pe _____ thus, tu _____
Accept incense, O thou very God!

ve - re De - - us!

During the following interlude the Three Kings lie down before the Manger and the Midwives place a coverlet over them.

52a

BELLS

All this being done, let the Magi fall asleep, there before the Manger, while an Angel appearing from above warns them in their dreams to return to their own land by another road.

Let the Angel say:

53

ARCHANGEL

p

Im - plé - ta sunt ó - mni - a quae pro - phé - ti - ce
Fulfilled are all the things of which the prophets have written.

scri - pta _____ sunt. I - te, vi - am ___ re - me - án -
When you are returning take another road;

46

thus you will not be informers to bring punishment to so great a King.

The Magi, having awakened:

54

3 KINGS

De - o grá - ti - as! _____
Thanks be to God!

Sur - gá - mus, er - go, vi - si - ó - ne mó - ni - ti
Let us, then, arise, being warned by the vision of the Angel,

an - gé - li - ca, Et, ____ cal le mu - tá - to,
and, by changing our way,

lá - te -ant He - ró - dem quae ví - di -mus de _____ pú - e - ro.
keep hidden from Herod what we have seen concerning the Child.

Then let the Magi, departing by another road without Herod seeing
them, sing:

55

3 KINGS

O, ____ ad - mi - rá - bi - le com - mer - ci - um!
O admirable understanding;

Cre - á - tor gé - ne - ris hu - má - ni, a - ni - má - tum
the Creator of the human race, assuming a human body,

cor - pus sú - mens, de Vir - gi - ne ná - sci di -gná - tus· est:
vouchsafed to be born of a Virgin;

et pro - cé - dens ho - mo si - ne _____ sé - mi - ne,
and becoming man without earthly seed,

lar - gí - tus est no - bis su - am ___ de - i - tá - tem.
bestow'd upon each of us his divinity.

The Magi, led by the Star, process in the chancel as they sing "O admira-
bile . . ." and then take their places before the audience in the nave. The
Midwives and Angel Choir also begin their recessional.

55a

ANGEL CHOIR
MIDWIVES

O, _____ ad - mi - rá - bi - le com - mer - ci - um!
O admirable understanding;

Cre - á - tor gé - ne - ris hu - má - ni, a - ni - má - tum
the Creator of the human race, assuming a human body,

cor - pus sú - mens, de Vir - gi - ne ná - sci di - gná - tus _ est:
vouchsafed to be born of a Virgin;

et pro - cé - dens ho - mo si - ne _____ sé - mi - ne,
and becoming man without earthly seed,

lar - gí - tus est no - bis su - am ___ de - i - tá - tem.
bestow'd upon each of us his divinity.

Singing to the audience:

56

3 KINGS

Gáu - - de - te, fra - tres; _ Chri - stus no - bis _
Let us rejoice, O brothers;   Christ our Lord is born for us;

na - tus _____ est; De - us ho - mo _ fac - tus _ est!
                                    God is now made man!

The Three Kings repeat No. 55 and continue their recessional following the Star down the center aisle to the rear of the nave:

56a

3 KINGS

O, _____ ad - mi - rá - bi - le com - mer - ci - um!
O   admirable understanding;

Cre - á - tor gé - ne - ris hu - má - ni, a - ni - má - - tum
the Creator of the human race,   assuming a human body,

cor - pus sú - mens, de Vir - gi - ne ná - sci di - gná - tus _ est:
                              vouchsafed to be born of a Virgin;

et pro - cé - dens ho - mo si - ne _____ sé - mi - ne,
and becoming man without earthly seed,

lar - gí - tus est no - bis su - am _ de - i - tá - tem.
bestow'd upon each of us his divinity.

49

II *The Slaying of the Children*

At the "Slaying of the Children" the Innocents are clothed in white garments and while going joyously about the monastic church they pray
to God, thus:

*It is here suggested that "O quam gloriosum . . ." first be sung by the
Archangel to enable the Innocents to enter the nave and proceed slowly
down the center aisle behind a child carrying a medallion (or banner) on
a pole depicting a Lamb carrying a cross. Immediately following the
Archangel the Children repeat No. 1 joyously.*

A - gnum __ quo - cúm - que ___ í - e - rit.

wheresoever He goes.

Then the Lamb, carrying a cross and coming unexpectedly, goes before
them hither and thither while those following sing:

2

BELLS

CHILDREN

E - mít - te A - gnum, Dó - mi - ne ___

Send forth to us, O Lord, the Lamb,

do - mi - na - tó - rem ___ ter - rae, ___

the Ruler of the whole earth,

de pe - tra ___ de - ser - ti ___

from stony waste

ad ___ mon - tem _ fi - li - ae ___ Si - on. ___

to the mount of the daughter of Zion.

*The Children follow the Lamb to down-stage left. Herod, his Son,
Armiger and his Musician enter throne area from up-stage right.*

Meanwhile, a certain Armiger offers to the seated Herod his scepter,
saying:

3 **Pompously**

ARMIGER

Su - per ___ só - li - um Da - vid, ___

He shall sit on David's throne,

et su - per re - gnum e - ius se - dé - bit in ae - tér - num. ___

and over this his kingdom he shall reign for evermore.

Meanwhile, an Angel appears above the Manger and warns Joseph to
flee into Egypt with Mary. The Angel thrice addresses Joseph:

4   **With urgency—3 times**

BELLS

ARCHANGEL

Jó - seph, Jó - seph, Jó - seph,   fi - li Da - vid!
Joseph, Joseph, Joseph,   son of David!

As the Archangel calls, Joseph enters the chancel and goes to the Man-
ger.

Then he continues:

5

BELLS   *Bells continue on this note at random while the Archangel sings.*

ARCHANGEL

Tol - le pú - e - rum ___ et ma - trem ___ e - ius,
Take the young child and also his mother,

et va - de in ___ Ae - gy - - - ptum, ___
and seek the land of Egypt,

et es - to i - bi ___ us - que ___ dum di - cam ti - bi.
and in it remain even until I tell thee.

Fu - tú - rum est ___ e - nim ___ ut ___ He - ró - - des ___
For it will come to pass that King Herod himself

quae - rat pú - e - rum ___ ad per - dén - dum ___ e - um.
will seek out the child to destroy him.

Joseph takes Mary and Child out of the Manger and leaves the chancel
from stage left as he sings No. 6.

Joseph, unseen by Herod, departs with Mary carrying the Child. He says:

6

JOSEPH

Æ - gy - pte, no - li fle — — re!
Land of Egypt, weep no more!

qui - a _____ do - mi - ná - - tor tu - us
Since thy Ruler

ve - ni - et ti - - - bi, _____
before whose countenance all the might of the pit of Hell is made to tremble,

an - te cu - ius con - spé - - ctum mo - ve - bún - tur

a - bys - si, Li - be - rá - re póp - u - lum _____
cometh to thee to liberate thy people

su - - um _____ de má - nu _____ po - tén - ti - -
from the hands of the men of power.

um. _____ Ec - ce _____ do - mi - ná - tor Dó - mí - nus
Behold, the great one, the Omnipotent, is coming unto us.

cum vir - tú - te _____ vé - ni - - et.

Meanwhile the Armiger first salutes the King and, announcing that the
Magi have returned by a different road, says:

7 **Furiously**

ARMIGER

Rex, _____ in ae - tér - num ___ vi - ve!
O King, live thou for ever!

De - lú - sus es, ___ Dó - mi - ne: Ma - gi vi - am ___
Thou art deceiv'd, O master;   the Magi have returned by another

re - di - é - runt _____ á - li - am!
road!

Thereupon Herod, as though he were shattered, seizes a sword and prepares to slay himself, but is prevented from doing so by his attendants
and is pacified saying:

8 **Passionately**

HEROD

In - cén - di - um me - um ru - ín - a _____ res - tín - guam!
My death would extinguish this my burning passion!

Meanwhile, the Innocents, still walking behind the Lamb sing the following:

9 **With motion**

BELLS

CHILDREN

A - gno ___ sa - cra - to pro
Unto the Sacred Lamb,   the

no - bis mor - ti - fi - cá - to splen - dó - rem pá -
Christ who was sacrificed for us,   We offer, under that same token of light, The

55

tris, splen - dó - rem _ Vir - gi - ni - tá - tis, of - fé - ri - mus
splendour of the Father, the splendour of virginity.

Chri - sto sub si - gno _ lú - mi - nis is - to. Mul - tis
From the wrath

i - ra mo - dis ut _ quos in - qúi - rit He - ró - dis A -
of Herod, who has sought for us in many ways.
We shall be

gno _ sal - vé - mur, cum Chri - sto con - mo - ri - é - mur.
saved by the Lamb, that we may share in death with Christ.

The tempo of all pieces from #9 to #13a should remain the same

The Armiger, speaking to Herod, makes this suggestion:

ARMIGER

Di - scér - ne, __ Dó - mi - ne, vin - di - cá - re _
You must now determine, Lord, whether thus to vent your anger,

i - ram _ tu - am, Et __ strí - cto mu - cró - ne iú - be oc -
Or to issue the strictest order to put

cí - - di pú - e - ros.
these children to the sword!

For - te in - ter oc -
For perchance among the dead,

ci - sos oc - ci - dé - tur _ et ____ Chri - stus. ____
it may be found that Christ has perish'd.

Herod, handing him a sword, says:

11

DRUM

HEROD

mf

Ar - mi - ger ex - í - mi -
Armour bearer, great in worth:

e; Pú - e - ros fac ____ en - se pe - rí - re!
See that by the sword the children are slain!

Meanwhile, as the slayers approach, the Lamb secretly withdraws and
the Innocents acclaim him as he departs.

12

DRUM

BELLS

CHILDREN

f

Sal - ve, A - gnus De - i!
Hail, thou Lamb of God!

Sal - ve qui tol - lis pec -
who takest away the sins of the world!

cá - ta mun - di! Al - le - lu - ia!

Here Herod's Soldiers enter, swords held high and join Herod and his court singing:

12a

DRUM

HEROD
ARCHELAUS
ARMIGER
SOLDIERS

Rex est natus fór - ti - or, No - bis
Yet we hear of a greater still, who as a kingly babe is

et po - tén - ti - or. Vé - re - or ne só - li -
born. Truly there is fear that we

o Nos ex - trá - het ré - gi - o!
may from our royal throne be torn!

Con - tra il - lum ré - gu - lum, Con - tra
'Gainst that king of little worth, 'gainst the babe, new

na - tum pár - vu - lum, Iu - be, pa - ter, fí - li -
brought to birth, Give word, father, to thy son,

um Hoc in - í - re proe - li - um!
that this war be now begun.

The Mothers of the victims then intercede with the slayers.

13

DRUM

MOTHERS CONSOLERS

O - ré - mus, te - né - rè na - tó - rum pár - ci - te vi - tae! _____
We pray you to spare the tender lives of these infants!

13a

DRUM

This drum beat continues until the Soldiers and Herod's Musician leave chancel by up-stage right.

Afterwards, when the victims have fallen, an Angel from above addresses them, saying:

14   **A bit slower**

ARCHANGEL

Vos __ qui in púl - ve - re es ___ - tis,
Rouse ye and lift up your voices, ye who have fallen prostrate in the dust.

ex - per - gi - scí - mi - ni ___ et __ clá - ma - te.

The prostrate Children:

15

CHILDREN

Qua - re non de - fén - - dis sán - gui - nem __
Thou who art our father, why do you not defend us from destruction?

no - strum, _____ De - us nos - ter? _____

It is best perhaps to have one boy sing this.

The Angel:

16

ARCHANGEL

Ad - huc sus - ti - né - te mó - di - cum __ tem - - pus _____
Remain here but for a little while,

do - nec — im - ple - á - tur — nú - me - rus frá - -
until you join again   *the company of your brethren.*

trum ves - - - tró - - rum! _____
trum ves —

Rachel enters while the Archangel sings.

Rachel is then brought in with two Consolers:
Standing over the Children she laments, sometimes falling, saying:

17   **Moderately fast—same tempo continues through #20**

RACHEL

He - u! te - né - ri par - tus — lá - ce -
Ah! alas! you tender babes!   *Such savage wounds we*

ros — quos cér - ni - mus ar tus! He - u! dul - ces — na -
are viewing!   *Ah! alas! you sweet infants,*

ti, _____ so - la rá - bi - e ju - gu - lá - ti!
doom'd to death by a deed of madness!

He - u! quem — nec pí - e - tas nec _____
Ah! alas! that neither years   *nor tender affection could*

ves - tra co - ér - cu - it ae - tas! He - u! ma tres —
save you!   *Piteous mothers, ah!*

mi - sé - rae, quae _____ có - gi - mur is - ta vi - dé - re!
that you should have to realize what we have witness'd!

He - u! quid — nunc — á - gi - mus! Cur non haec fac - ta
What shall we now do? alas!   *We cannot bear such happenings!*

sú - bi - mus! He - u! qui - a — mé - mo - res no -
All these memories of ours, Alas!

stró - que le - vá - re do - ló - res. Gau - di - a non.___
can but serve to renew our grief! No more can there be gladness,

pos -sunt nam ___ dul - ci - a pi - gnó - ra de - sunt!
since our sweet pledges of love have perished!

The Consolers *(Mothers)* support her as she falls, saying:

18

2 CONSOLERS
(2 MOTHERS)

No - li, ___ vir - go — Ra - chel, no - li dul -
Do not, O pure Rachel, do not, O sweetest of

cis - si - ma ma - ter, pro _____ ne - ce par -
mothers, Cease weeping in sorrow for the children who

vó - rum fle - tus re - ti - né - re do - ló - rum.
here lie slain.

Si quae tris - tá - ris, ex - úl - ta — quae la - cri -
But, as you mourn so, rejoice in the tears you render,

má - ris. Nam - que tu i na - ti
Since that these your offspring live as the blessed in heaven.

vi - vunt su - per as - tra be - á - ti.

Rachel continues her lament:

19

RACHEL

He - u! he - u! he - u! Qúo - mo - do gau -
How can I be joyful;

dé - bo; dum mor - tu - a mem - bra ví - dé - bo;
forever these mangled limbs seeing;

Dum sic com - mó - ta fú - e - ro per
When my whole being is so rended by emotion?

vi - sce - ra to - ta? Me fa - cí - ent ve - re
Truly these sweet children will mean to me perpetual grieving!

pú - e - ri sí - ne fi - ne do - lé - re. O
Oh,

do - lor! O
sorrow! *Oh,*

pa - trum mu - tá - ta - que gáu - di - a ma -
how changed the joy of these parents' devotion

trum ad lu - gú - bres luc - tus! La - cri -
Into grief and mourning! *Freely let your tears*

má - rum fún - di - te fle - tus, Ju - daé - ae flo -
be flowing, *Mourning Judea's flow'r,*

rem pá - tri - ae la - cri - mán - do do - ló - rem!
telling of the Fatherland's sorrow!

The Consolers again:

20

5 CONSOLERS
MOTHERS

Quid ___ tu, ___ vir - go, ma - ter ___ Ra - chel,
Why do you weep so,

Rachel, mother, lovely in sorrow,

plo - ras for - mo - sa, cu - ius ___
You in whose countenance Jacob

vul - tus Ja - cob de - lec - tat? ce -
doth delight?

Even as a

u so - ro - ris an - ní - cu - le ___
baby sister

lip - pi - tú - do e - um ___
would bring solace to his weary eyes!

iú - vat! Ter - ge, ___ ma - ter
Dry your brimming eyes, O mother!

flen - tes ___ ó - cu - los!. Quam te ___
Rivers of tears do not become your

de - cent ge - na - rum ___ ri - vu - li?
cheek.

Then Rachel:

21

Quickly

RACHEL

He - u, He - u, He - u! Quid me in - cu - sá - stis fle - tus in - cás - sum fu - dís - se?
Wherefore do you say that I have shed these tears so vainly?

Cum sim or - bá - ta na - to, pau - per - tá - tem me - am qui so - lus cu - rá - ret;
Being bereft of my son, who alone my poverty would have cared for;

Qui non hós - ti - bus cé - de - ret an - gús - tos tér - mi - nos,
who would not to an enemy the smallest portion yield,

quos mi - hi Ja - cob ad - qui - sí - vit, Quí - que stó - li - dıs frá - tri - bus,
which Jacob had acquir'd for me, To the many callous citizens

quos mul - tos, proh do - lor, ex - tu - li, es - set pro - fu - tú - rus?
what matters it, when, alas!, he is carried to the grave?

Then the Consolers, lifting the fallen Children, say:

22 **Slower**

5 CONSOLERS
MOTHERS

p

Num. quid flen - dus est is - te,
Why must you weep for the child,

qui re - gnum pos - si - det cae - lés - te.
when he has gained a heavenly kingdom?

Quid - que prae - ce fre - qúen - te mí - se - ris
Whatever may be, he will be help'd by the frequent and sorrowful prayers of his brethren?

frá - tri - bus a - pud De - um au - xi - li - é - tur?

Again Rachel, falling upon the Children:

23 **Somewhat slower**

RACHEL

p

An - xi - á - tus est in me spi - ri - tus me - us;
Great is the anguish which possesses my spirit;

in ___ me tur ― bá ― tum est ___ cor ___ me ― um.
within me my heart is troubled.

The Consolers then lead Rachel away and meanwhile an Angel from on
high utters the following antiphon:

24 **Quicker**

BELLS

Bells continue on this note at random through No. 24.

ARCHANGEL

Sí ― ni ― te pár ― vu ― los ve ― ní ― re ___ ad me,
Suffer little children to come unto me,

tá ― li ― um est é ― nim ___ re ― gnum cae ― ló ― rum.
for such is the Kingdom of heaven.

The Children rise up at the sound of the Angels' voices, saying as they
enter the choir:

*The Bell notes are played at random while No. 25 is sung 3 times: the
first time by the Children, the second adding Mothers, and finally with
Consolers. The Bells should conclude on "G".*

25

BELLS

CHILDREN

O _____ Chri ― ste,
How numerous, O Christ, is the youthful army of the Father,

quan ― tum ___ pa ― tri e ― xér ― ci ― tum Iú ― ve ― nis ___

do ― ctus ___ ad bel ― la ___ má ― xi ― ma; _____
vers'd in the great battles:

pó - pu - lis práe - di - cans, _____ col - li - gis, ____
So much tragedy they proclaim to the people,

um - bras sug - gens cum _ tan - tum _ mí - se - ris.
seeming a gathering of shades.

The Children slowly ascend to their former place as Angels. The slayers and Rachel gather at down-stage left and look toward the Archangel as they sing. The Fleury MS. stage instruction (below) indicates a dumb show for Herod's death and the crowning of Archelaus. Perhaps Armiger should summon two Soldiers to carry the dead King off and then present Archelaus with Herod's crown and scepter.

While this has been going on, Herod has died and in his place Archelaus, his Son, reigns as King. Meanwhile in Egypt, whither Joseph previously fled, an Angel advises him saying:

26

BELLS

ARCHANGEL

Jó - seph, Jó - seph. Jó - seph, fi - li Da - vid!
Joseph, Joseph, Joseph, son of David!

At the sound of the Archangel's call, Joseph and Mary appear and take their place down-stage center.

"g" Bell plays at random while Archangel sings.

Re - vér - te - re in __ ter - ram Jú - dam;
Return now to the land of Judea;

de - fún - cti sunt é - - nim _ qui _
those enemies have perish'd   who once did

quae - ré - bant _ á - ni - mam __ pú - e - ri.
seek the life of the child.

Thereupon Joseph returns with Mary and the Child, withdrawing into
the region of Galilee, saying:

27 **Joyously**

JOSEPH

Gau - de, gau - de, — gau - de, Ma - rí - a Vir - go;
Rejoice, rejoice, rejoice, O Virgin Mary;

cun - ctas háe - re -ses, so - la in - tem - e - ri - sti in un - i - vér - so mun - do.
Thou alone hast caus'd all the false beliefs in the world to be brought to nothing.

The Cantor *(Joseph)* begins Te Deum Laudamus:

BELLS

Bells for the "Te Deum" to be played evenly to the end.

JOSEPH

Te Dé - um lau - da - mus: ——

BOYS AND WOMEN

Te — ae - tér - num Pá - trem

MEN

te Dó - mi -num con - fi - té - mur.

o - mnis — tér - ra ve - ne - rá, - tur.

Ti - bi ó -mnes An - ge - li,

ti - bi ___ caé - li et u - ni - vér - sae po - te – stá – tes:

Tí – bi Ché - ru - bim et Sé – ra – phim in - ces – sá - bi - li

vó - ce pro - clá – mant:

Sán – – ctus: ___

Sán – – ctus: ___

Sán – – ctus ___

Plé – ni sunt caé - li et tér – ra

Dó - mi - nus Dé - us __ Sá - ba – oth.

ma - je – stá – tis gló - ri - ae __ tú – ae.

Te __ glo - ri - ó _ - sus A - pos - to - ló -rum __ chó _ - rus:

Te __ Pro -phe - tá _ - rum lau- dá- bi - lis __ nú - me - rus:

Te __ Már- ty -rum can-di - dá - tus láu-dat ex - ér - ci - tus.

Te __ per ór -bem ter -rá _ - rum sán - cta __ con - fi - té - tur

Ec - clé - si - a:

Pá - - trem _____

Ve - ne-rán-dum tú - um vé - rum,

im - mén - sae ma - je - stá - tis:

a - pe – ru - í -sti cre -dén -ti -bus ré – gna cae - ló – rum.

Tu ad — déx -te -ram Dé - i sé – des, ____

in gló – ri - a — pá – tris.

Iú – dex cré – de - ris

Te er – go quaé -su -mus,

és – se ven - tú – rus.

tú - is fá - mu - lis súb – ve – ni, quos pre – ti - ó - so

sán -gui - ne — red -e – mi - sti.

Ae - tér – na — fac ____

cum sán - ctis tú - is in gló - ri - a nu - me - rá - ri.

Sál - vum __ fac pó - pu - lum tú - um Dó - mi - ne, __

et bé - ne - dic hae - re - di - tá - ti __ tú - ae.

Et ré - ge é - os, __ et ex - tól - le il - los

us - que in ae - tér - num.

Per sin - gu - los __ di - es, __

be - ne - di - ci - mus te.

Et lau - dá - mus nó - men tú - um

in saé - cu - lum, et in saé - cu - lum __ saé - cu - li.

Dí - gná - re Dó - mi - ne dí - e i - sto _____

si - ne __ pec - cá - to nos __ cu - sto - di - re.

Mi - se - ré - re

no - stri Dó - mi - ne, mí - se - ré - re __ nó - stri.

Fi - at — mi - se - ri - cór - di - a tú - a Dó - mi - ne

su - per — nos, quem ad - mó - dum spe - rá - vi - mus in te.

In te — Dó - mi - ne spe - ra - - vi: —

non con - fún - dar — in ae - tér - - num.

Thus it ends.

74

Historical Notes

[The material transcribed by W. L. Smoldon from a twelfth-century manuscript, the "Fleury play-book," belonging originally to the monastery of St. Benoît-sur-Loire near Fleury in N. France, and now in the Municipal Library at Orléans (MS 201).]

SOURCES

The rise and full development of the Latin music-dramas of the medieval Church seem to have occupied over three centuries, from the second part of the tenth to the end of the thirteenth.[1] The earliest dramas, emerging from a brief invented dialogue (the "Quem quaeritis" trope) attached to the Introit of the Easter Mass, were concerned with the events at the Sepulchre on the first Easter morning.[2] Dramatic action only became possible when this dialogue was transferred from the Mass to the end of Matins.

1. It is important to distinguish the liturgical music-dramas of the Church, *sung* in *Latin* within church walls by clerics, from the later emergence, the mystery-plays, drama *spoken* in the *vernacular* in the open air by secular actors. In the case of the church dramas (to judge by the rubrics) the vocal line seems to have been given only very occasional instrumental assistance, and this from organ and from chime-bells *(cymbala)*. In the case of the mystery-plays the practice of incidental music gave professional instrumentalists ample opportunity to exercise their art.

2. A bilingual acting-version of an Easter Sepulchre drama *(Visitatio Sepulchri)*, associated with the monastery of Fleury and transcribed and edited by the present writer, has been published by the Oxford University Press (London).

Gradually dramas were expanded to include further happenings on Easter Day, and finally later incidents of the Easter season. By the eleventh century other dramas had developed, attached to the Christmas season. The earliest and simplest were concerned with the Gospel story of the Shepherds in the field and at the Manger, and arose similarly from a trope of a Mass—the third of Christmas ("Quem quaeritis in praesepe, pastores?"). Real expansion awaited the development of the story of the Star-led Magi, together with incidents concerning Herod and his court.

About a dozen of the "Magi" dramas survive, of which the one under consideration is perhaps the most attractive. The simplest, an eleventh-century example from Nevers Cathedral (the "Magi" dramas seem to have been a French development), consists of something over a dozen prose items, a mixture of actual antiphons, adaptations of them and other liturgical texts, settings of sentences from the Gospels, together with a certain amount of new invention—words and music. The material as given in the Nevers version can be thought of as representing a common "core," employed by all the other Magi dramas, with their own individual additions, omissions, adaptations, and versifyings.[3] The Fleury version with which we are dealing is particularly original in dealing with basic material. One of the fullest of the Magi dramas, containing in one shape or another most of the material found in other versions, is that from the cathedral of Freising, and dates from the eleventh century. The development of the type must therefore have been complete by then. With regard to the figures of the three Shepherds, there have survived a few examples, founded on the Christmas trope and the account in St. Luke, II, of a brief and separate *Officium Pastorum.* This shows the Shepherds being informed by the vision of the Angel and journeying to the Manger, where they adore the newborn Child after being questioned by two "Midwives" *(obstetrices)* who, without any Gospel sanction and derived from a second-century tradition, are represented as being present. Most of the Magi dramas make but slight use of the Shepherds, or else ignore them. They are chiefly represented as *returning* from the Manger, meeting and replying to the questing Magi who are on their way to it. Our Magi drama from Fleury, however, gives generous length to the scene of the Angels in the heights and the Shepherds in the field, together with the adoration at the Manger. The incident of the meeting of Magi and Shepherds is made the occasion of two major items by the latter.

3. The most important examples are from Compiègne, and from the cathedrals of Freising and Nevers—all these of the eleventh century; from Sicily (Norman-French), Strassburg, Rouen (Montpellier), and from the monasteries of Fleury and Bilsen—all these of the twelfth century. A full-scale version from the cathedral of Laon, of the thirteenth century, shows familiar textual details but no music. In several thirteenth- and fourteenth-century Rouen Cathedral manuscripts the figures of the Magi (as the Three Kings) are associated with the oblation ceremony of the Epiphany Mass. Here, the items characteristic of the Magi dramas are cut down to the level of the Nevers version. It seems difficult to decide whether the Magi type of drama was first inspired by the gift-bearing oblation ceremony contained in the Mass, or that the intrusion of the robed and crowned Kings into the official rite was suggested by the prior existence of such a histrionic form.

The main inspiration for the various incidents in the Epiphany dramas being the second chapter of St. Matthew, it is surprising to find that only three of the surviving examples carry forward the story dramatically to include the Gospel account of the slaying of the young children that was ordered by Herod. The others of the group either end with the escape of the Magi or add some brief sentences which merely reveal Herod's cruel intentions. Of those that stage the massacre, the thirteenth-century Laon manuscript (without music) does indeed include the incident within the framework of a single drama. The playwright-composers of Fleury and Freising, however, chose to develop separate ones, under the headings of *Ad Interfectionem Puerorum . . .* and *Ordo Rachelis.* The second title signalizes the fact that, under the inspiration of St. Matthew II, 17-18, and the prophet Jeremiah, the figure of Rachel is made to be the leader of the mourning mothers. The dramas also include the incident of the Flight into Egypt. Once again it is the Fleury version which handles its material with by far the greatest artistry.[4]

Before considering the two Fleury dramas in detail some note will be taken of the manuscript (the "Fleury play-book") from which they come. As we have already seen, this belonged originally to the Benedictine monastery of St. Benoît-sur-Loire where the two occur successively among a miscellaneous group of ten. As ever, the identity of the creator (or creators) is not known. Although the whole of the dramas were written apparently by a single hand, the individual works vary so much in treatment and quality that one might well conclude that they represented a collection, the units not necessarily originating at the monastery. But the Fleury community was famous during the medieval centuries for its brilliant literary activities, and one can readily believe that it could only have been Fleury that put together the *Ordo ad representandum Herodem,* the *Interfectio Puerorum . . .,* the *Visitatio Sepulchri,* and even the *Pere-*

4. In considering dramas of the "Slaying" I have disregarded as of small import a brief dramatic scene in verse between Rachel and a consoling Angel, found in an eleventh-twelfth-century Limoges manuscript.

grinus, which are at a much more satisfactory dramatic level than, say, *Tres Clerici, Tres Filiae*, or *De Resuscitatione Lazari*. The two "Herod" works, besides representing the best dramatic treatment of their themes, are quite generous in their rubric details as to action. These cast a great deal of light on the manner in which they were first presented. Although perhaps belonging to different feasts ("Magi" at Epiphany—the "Slaying" on Innocents' Day) there can be little objection to staging the two as an entity, since the action is continuous, and as we have seen, there is already one example, a thirteenth-century manuscript from Laon, which definitely blends the two themes in a single drama.

THE PLAY OF HEROD—THE MEDIEVAL PRODUCTION

It must be recalled that these various medieval church-dramas, whether for Easter, Christmas, or saint-day, were intended as religious instruction—designed "to fortify the faith of the unlettered vulgar and of neophytes," as St. Ethelwold's *Regularis Concordia* puts it. The actions took place wholly within church walls, usually between the end of Matins and the concluding Te Deum; sometimes at Vespers; while a few examples actually lead into the Mass itself. The actors were clerics of various grades. There is one instance known of a bishop taking part. Choir boys were used. Lest the modern employment of women be thought of as an anachronism, let it be stated that there is firm evidence as to nuns' being employed (in the parts of the Marys) in what would have been "mixed casts." The present writer readily recalls half a dozen examples, ranging over France, the Germanic countries, Italy, and England. Regarding the matter of dramatic expression, manuscript rubrics often clearly encourage displays of deep feeling. A fourteenth-century *Planctus* at the Cross from Cividale, made up of about a score of stanzas, contains (exceptionally, it is true) close on eighty directions concerned with emotional actions and gestures. As for costuming, in the early stages of the dramas in general

there was much adaptation of the ordinary vestments of the sacristy (e.g. albs for angels; dalmatics with amices used as head wrappings, or even copes, for the "women"). Examples of a greater realism are sometimes found in the more developed dramas, concerned with the more important figures. The rubrics of the two Fleury dramas are, however, not very informative on the point. Herod's Courtiers are "dressed as young men," the Scribes are "bearded," the Innocents wear "white garments." No details are given as to how the principals are attired, but in other Magi versions we read of crowns, silken garments, and staves for the Three Kings. However, much other information is given, enabling us to visualize the *mise-en-scène* of the medieval performance in the ample spaces of the monastic church. The Manger, which has survived into modern times as the Christmas Crib, and which, to judge by evidence from other Christmas dramas, was curtained to hide from view the effigies of Mother and Child until the moment of revelation, was situated somewhere in the nave near one of the doors.[5] An important stage property was the Star, apparently a candelabrum, which, again to judge by the rubrics of other dramas, was hung on high and drawn from place to place by means of a cord. In the Fleury rubrics it is first discovered shining above the high altar, and later we are told that it "advances" and "leads" the Magi. "Jerusalem" was apparently a playing space situated in front of the choir doors. Somewhere near at hand, perhaps on some kind of platform, was "Herod's court." Elsewhere, probably a mere space in the nave, was the field of the Shepherds. The Angels, "above," may have appeared in one of the galleries. It must be remembered that the medieval nave was unencumbered by seating, and the space available for action stretched from west end to high altar. Other properties mentioned include the "strange burdens" of the Magi, which prove to be the traditional gifts of gold, frankincense, and myrrh. Also detailed are the swords of Herod and his son, Archelaus, while the latter makes

5. Since in the Fleury version of the "Innocents" Joseph leads Mary to and from "the land of Egypt" she must here probably have been represented by a living person.

reference to his father's sceptre. A "Book of the Prophets" was also needed. In the second drama, the "Innocents," comes the mysterious and symbolic appearance with the children of "a Lamb carrying a cross," who "goes before them hither and thither." How the "Lamb" was originally represented is not made clear. In the present modern performance a large medallion mounted on a tall standard was employed, together with a "standard-bearer." A similar device replaced the potentially risky procedure of a high-suspended and cord-drawn "Star."

THE PLAY OF HEROD—THE TEXTS

A reading of the texts as given in this edition will confirm what has already been said as to the nature of the texts of these Christmas dramas in general. In the main, Fleury uses prose passages, occasionally of some length, but more often in the form of brief dialogue exchanges. In contrast to these are more occasional items in regular rhyming lines of Latin poetry. A number of the longer prose passages, and even some of the shorter ones, are actual liturgical antiphons or other service pieces, relevant to the situation and skilfully adapted. Also there are a couple of phrases that suggest that their inventor was well acquainted with the *Aeneid*. On the whole, however, the numerous interchanges of prose dialogue at Herod's court—the King, Armiger, the other court officials, the Magi—represent free composition. In both dramas the textual borrowings from the Gospel accounts are relatively slight, the most notable being items from the opening Shepherd scene, and, at the court, the prophetic utterance read to Herod.

Regarding items in rhyming verse, there are three such in the "Magi" part of the drama. The first (No. 15—"Caldei sumus . . .") is sung by the Three Kings at their first encounter with Herod's court in the person of Armiger. It may represent a borrowing on Fleury's part, since the stanza occurs also in the eleventh-century Freising manuscript, though with different music. The second is an exchange between Herod and Archelaus (Nos. 39 to 41—"Salve, pater inclyte . . ."). The poem is found also in the

"Montpellier" drama of the same century (without music), so Fleury's authorship must remain in doubt. The third (No. 47—"Quem non praevalent . . .") occurs in varied shapes in several other Magi versions, and indeed represents modifications of an ancient liturgical "sequence," a type of composition which was sung chorally and in antiphonal style, each pair of lines having the same melody. To anticipate musical findings I mention here that the Fleury setting is *not* that of the sequence, and seems to be an original one. Besides these three major items, there are occasional rhyming couplets, clearly intended as verse.

In the "Innocents" part of the drama not only is a greater use made of liturgical adaptations (the children, Joseph, Rachel, even Armiger all employ relevant antiphons) but there is a greater proportion of lines in regular poetic rhythm. The skilfully constructed "Agno sacrato . . ." stanza of the Innocents (No. 9) seems to be Fleury's own invention, but the great emotional scene of the drama, Rachel's lament and the intervention of her Consolers, represents a dovetailing of several different elements. Her first rhyming solo (No. 17—"Heu, teneri . . .") has lines found also in the Freising play, but the "Noli, virgo Rachel . . ." (No. 18) occurs elsewhere only in the thirteenth-century Laon manuscript, and the stanza may well be Fleury's own. Rachel's renewed lament continues in the same poetic rhythm, but it is to be noted that two of the lines can be found in the Freising version. With the resumption of the Consolers' chorus a strange new adaptation can be recognized; from "Quid tu, virgo . . ." (No. 20) to the end of No. 22 (". . . Deum auxilietur") the text consists of a tenth-century sequence by the famous monk, Notker of St. Gall. Being of an early type its lines are irregular and it is without rhyme. Again anticipating the discussion of the musical setting, I mention that Fleury supplies its own melody, owing no debt to Notker. Rachel rounds off her scene with a liturgical antiphon (No. 23). This lament section may have sounded like a textual hotchpotch, but in fact the blending is done so skilfully as to make a homogeneous and effective libretto for one of the most remarkable examples of the use of dramatic melody that can be found in medieval times.

THE PLAY OF HEROD—THE MUSIC

As we have previously noted, the music supplied to any medieval church-drama was never more than that of a single line of vocal melody (as in the case of the liturgy). In a number of instances (mostly of the "breviary" type of manuscript) no music at all is given, but there is every reason to believe that the texts were nevertheless sung. Especially in the earlier centuries the musical settings took the form of *neumes*, a notation which gave only the approximate rise and fall of a melody, while indicating the number of notes to a single syllable. Such a system merely *reminded* the trained singer of a passage which he already had had to memorize. This was succeeded by a gradually developing scheme (the ancestor of our own) which, starting with one "pitch" line and progressing to four, fixed definitely the melodic identity of a note. Mensural values remained undefined, in what gradually became the familiar plainchant "square notation."

It happens fortunately that the two Fleury manuscripts have four-line staves for their music, making pitch quite certain except for places where the original scribe has been careless. Of the other "Magi" and "Innocents" dramas mentioned above, only the thirteenth- to fourteenth-century Rouen versions and the Norman-French example from Sicily show fixed pitches. The best that the rest can do is to use unheighted neumes. These however, through their details, make the identity of a melody reasonably certain when compared with the line readings, and confirm what has previously been said regarding a common "pool" of material in the "Magi" scenes. But whatever occasional parallels can be traced in Fleury's musical settings they seem to reflect an original mind and are the most satisfactory and polished among the surviving Christmas drama material.

In all church-drama manuscripts the texts and music are set down in continuous fashion, broken only by the occurrence of rubrics and illumi-

nated capitals. Thus the transcriber, dealing, say, with any Easter or Christmas drama, will find that one of his tasks is to pick out from the prose sentences those which happen to scan and rhyme, and are therefore intended to be recognized as Latin poetry. When he does so he finds that the musical setting also shows a regularity, and often enough repetitions of melodic phrase. The settings of our two dramas use a technique found in most Easter and Christmas dramas of any length. The prose passages of dramatic dialogue are set to a type of free melody not to be distinguished from the style of the short liturgical antiphon,[6] while relief is afforded by the occasional occurrence of stanzas the music of which the transcriber is usually able to resolve into a regular rhythm, trochaic, iambic, or even duple, which can be set down with modern barrings, it being always remembered that the medieval centuries knew of no such notational strait-jackets. Other medieval music-dramas such as Old and New Testament and Saint plays have librettos which are usually in the form of poems of stanza construction, frequently uniform in pattern, their settings capable of being rendered rhythmically throughout. These works, with their stanza tunes often much repeated, are on the whole much less satisfactory dramatically than those using the techniques illustrated by our two Fleury examples, although *Daniel* must be held to be the brilliant exception.

The settings of the dramatic prose passages of our two dramas show not only melodic attractiveness but subtle workings of melodic motifs of a few notes. Such patternings are particularly apparent in the Magi's music, and in that of those who encounter them at Herod's court. A particularly brilliant piece of dramatic recita-

---

6. According to the views of such scholars as Dom Gregory Murray and the late J. W. Vollaerts liturgical chant before about A.D. 1000 was *rhythmic*. Certain "interpretation" signs carried by the neumes of manuscripts belonging to earlier centuries should, they hold, be accepted as indicating a strict system of note-values, one twice the length of the other. As our particular manuscripts belong to a somewhat later and "corrupted" period of the chant and show none of the rhythmic signs I have no alternative but to render the prose settings as "free rhythm," while observing the usual cadence lengthenings.

tive is Rachel's emotional "Heu! . . . Quid me incusastis . . ." (II, No. 21).

Regarding the several genuine and fairly lengthy liturgical antiphons (e.g. "O regem caeli . . .," "O admirabile commercium . . .," "O quam gloriosum . . .," "Aegipte, noli flere, . . .") these retain their service settings,[7] but a number of other prose items which appear to be indistinguishable from them in style are compositions which cannot be traced to liturgical sources. Such for example are the first three items of the first scene, used not only by Fleury but by Rouen and one or two others of the group.

The Play of Herod is certainly outstanding in regard to its poetic items, which, when the rhythms of their settings are interpreted, turn out to have exceptionally charming and expressive melodies. There is no evidence that forbids us to credit Fleury as being the begetter of these. In the matter of mensural interpretations the trochaic "first rhythmic mode" appears to be the usual solution, but the angry stanzas of Herod and his son (I. Nos. 39-41) gain an additional vigour from the iambic "second mode."[8] The high point musically of the whole work is to me the scene of Rachel's Lament (from II, No. 17 onwards). This surely must be reckoned as one of the finest achievements of medieval melodic art. The subtlety of its pattern constructions will well reward close study, and the phrases of Rachel and her Consolers, repeated and varied as they are, are bound together by a constantly recurring and haunting cadence, which first occurs in the pleading phrase of the Mothers, "Oremus tenere natorum parcite vite!"

7. One of the trials of a transcriber is to find that a liturgical item, no doubt well known to the original scribe, and to any cleric of the time, is given as an "incipit" (i.e. only the first few words and notes are set down). If, as is often the case, the particular antiphon or responsory or sequence is "obsolete," then a great deal of detective work has often to be undertaken.

8. There are many differences of opinion among scholars regarding the rhythmic interpretations of the melodies of the troubadours and trouvères, which also were set down in no more than plainchant notation. The same problems arise in relation to the settings of the Latin poetry of the church-dramas. In my transcriptions I have tried to choose the rhythms which I thought best suited the scansions and stresses of the Latin.

EDITORIAL ADDITIONS

It will be found that certain of the items have for various practical reasons been given editorial repetitions. Thus, the importance of the figure of Armiger is underlined by his interception and relaying of messages to Herod, and his adding his own weight to the latter's orders. Again, the message of the prophet that is spoken by the Scribe, so deadly for Herod, is repeated in consternation by the whole court. At suitable moments the rhythmic pieces, Nos. 15, 41, and 47 of the first part, are all given repetitions, while during the action of the Slaughter, where nothing vocal occurs in the manuscript, the Mothers repeat their agonized "Oremus tenere . . ." against the Soldiers' savage "Contra illum . . .," Archelaus' declaration of war in No. 41. In this scene also a menacing use is made of an *ostinato* drum-beat. Two choral items have been added. While certain dramas give opportunity for processional entries or opening unison choruses, Fleury has no such provision. Use has therefore been made of the medieval Christmas sequence "Orientis partibus" ("The Prose of the Ass") set to the tune to which it was sung at Sens cathedral. During the solemn moments at the Manger, when the curtains are withdrawn to reveal the Christ-child and his Mother, a thirteenth-century three-part motet, "*Alleluia psallite . . .*," is sung by the Angel Choir.

Regarding musical accompaniments, the evidence for the employment of instruments during the acting of these church-dramas is almost wholly negative. Whatever use of them is made in modern stagings must depend upon the principles of good taste, and the fact that in medieval times the dramas were performed during the Hour services of the church, when a restricted use of organ and of chime-bells only was permitted.

There will be noticed the occasional editorial suggestion as to the use of simple *organum*— the singing of a second part to the given one at the distance of a fifth or fourth, which in the period might have been introduced extempore.

W. L. SMOLDON

The Play of Herod

LITERAL TRANSCRIPTION

The following literal transcription of the pages of the "Fleury play-book" (Orléans MS 201, pp. 205-220) from which *The Play of Herod* in its acting-version form has been derived, sets out the texts and music of the two dramas, as far as possible in accordance with the original, here reproduced alongside. The musical notation is, for the sake of clarity, rendered in "black semibreve" form. The non-specialist will probably find it easier to follow than Gregorian notation. Through the use of slurs it manages still to keep plain the syllabic neume-groupings. Light "linking-notes" (*liquescents*) are indicated by smaller size black notes.

The editorial features, which have been sparingly added, are enclosed in pointed brackets ⟨ ⟩. The items themselves have been separated out, but it will be seen that in the original the scribe used every inch of space in continuous fashion, showing breaks only by illuminated capitals, heavy double bar-lines, and very occasional stops. I have written out in full words that were left abbreviated in the manuscript. Where the scribe has clearly blundered I have reproduced the original, but with due comment, and have made the correction in the acting-version.

Notes on certain features of the transcription are given after its conclusion.

W. L. SMOLDON

⟨ I THE REPRESENTATION OF HEROD⟩

Tunc incipit Ordo ad representandum Herodem.

Parato Herode et ceteris personis, tunc quidam Angelus cum multitudine in excelsis appareat. Quo viso, Pastores perterriti; salus annunciet eis de ceteris adhuc tacentibus:

Et subito omnis multitudo cum Angelo dicat:

82

Tunc demum surgentes cantent intra se *Transeamus,* et cetera:

3

Transeamus usque Bethleem, et videamus

hoc verbum quod factum est, quod fecit Dominus et ostendit nobis.

Et sic procedant usque ad precepe, quod ad januas monasterii paratum erit. Tunc
due Mulieres custodientes precepe interrogent Pastores, dicentes:

4

Quem queritis, pastores, dicite?

Respondeant Pastores:

5

Salvatorem Christum Dominum; infantem pannis involutum, secundum sermonem angelicum.

Mulieres:

6

Adest ⟨hic⟩ parvulus cum Maria matre eius, de qua dudum vaticinando Ysaias propheta

dixerat: "Ecce virgo concipiet et pariet filium."

Tunc Pastores procidentes adorent infantem dicentes:

7

Salve, Rex seculorum.

Postea surgentes invitent populum circumstantem adorandum infantem, dicentes
turbis vicinis:

8

Venite, venite, venite, adoremus Deum, quia ipse est Salvator noster.

Interim Magi prodeuntes, quisquam de angulo suo quasi de regione sua, conveniant
ante altare vel ortum Stelle, et dum appropinquant. Primus dicat:

9¹

Stella fulgore nimio rutilat!

Secundus:

9² Quem venturum olim propheta signaverat.

Tunc stantes collaterales, dicat dexter ad medium:

10¹ Pax tibi, frater!

Et ille respondeat:

10² Pax quoque tibi!

Et osculentur sese, sic medius ad sinistrum et sinister ad dextrum. Salutatio cuisque.
Tunc ostendant sibi mutuo ⟨et dicant⟩:

11 Ecce Stella! Ecce Stella! Ecce Stella!

Procedente autem Stella sequentur et ipsi precedentem Stellam, dicentes:

12 Eamus ergo et inquiramus eum, offerentes ei munera: aurum, thus et mirram; Quia scriptum didicimus:

Adorabunt eum omnes reges, omnes gentes servient ei.

Venientes ad hostium chori interrogent astantes:

13 Dicite nobis, O Jerosolimitani cives, ubi est expectatio gentium, ubi est qui natus est rex

Judeorum, quem signis celestibus agnitum venimus adorare?

Quibus visis, Herodes mittat ad eos Armigerum dicens:

14 Que rerum

novitas, aut que causa subegit vos ignotas temptare vias? Quo tenditis ergo? Quod genus? Unde

domo? Pacem ne huc fertis an arma?

Responsio Magorum:

15 Caldei sumus; pacem ferimus; regem regum querimus, quem natum esse stella indicat,

que fulgore ceteris clarior rutilat.

Armiger reversus salutat Regem; flexo genu dicat:

16 Vivat Rex in eternum!

⟨Herod:⟩

17 Salvet te gratia mea!

Armiger ad Regem:

18 Adsunt nobis, Domine, tres viri ignoti, ab oriente venientes, noviter natum quemdam regem queritantes.

Tunc mittat Herodes oratores vel interpretes suos ad Magos, dicentes:

19 Leti inquisitores, qui sunt inquirite reges, affore quos nostris iam fama revolvet in oris.

Interpretes ad Magos:

20 Principis edictu, reges,

prescire venimus quo sit profectus hic vester et unde profectus.

Magi:

21 Regem quesitum duce stella significatum; munere proviso properamus eum venerando.

Oratores reversi ad Herodem:

22 Reges sunt Arabum; cum trino munere; natum querunt infantem, quem monstrant sidera regem.

Herodes mittens Armigerum pro Magis:

23 Ante venire jube, quo possim singula scire qui sunt, cur veniant, quo nos rumore requirant.

Armiger:

24 Quod mandas, citius, Rex inclyte, perficietur.

Armiger ad Magos:

25 Regia vos mandata vocant; non segniter ite.

Armiger adducens Magos ad Herodem:

26 En Magi veniunt, et regem natum stella duce, requirunt.

Herodes ad Magos:

27 Que sit causa vie? Qui vos, vel unde venitis? Dicite.

Magi:

28 Rex est causa vie; Reges sumus ex Arabitis huc veni-

entes. Querimus en regem regnantibus imperitantem, Quem natum mundo lactat Judaica virgo.

Herodes ad Magos:

29 Regem, quem queritis, natum esse quo signo didicistis?

Magi:

30 Illum natum esse didicimus in Oriente, stella monstrante.

Herodes:

31 Si illum regnare creditis, Dicite nobis?

Magi:

32 Illum regnare fatentes, cum mysticis muneribus de terra longinqua adorare venimus, trinum Deum

venerantes tribus cum muneribus.

Tunc ostendant munera.

33 Primus dicat: Auro regem. Secundus: Thure Deum. Tertius: Mirra mortalem.

Tunc Herodes imperet Simistis qui cum eo sedent in habitu juvenili, ut adducant
Scribas qui in diversorio parati sunt barbati:

34 Vos mei Simiste, legis peritos ascite ut discant in Prophetis quid sentiant ex his.

Simiste ad Scribas, et adducant eos cum libris Prophetarum:

35 Vos, legis periti ad regem vocati, cum Prophetarum libris properando venite.

Postea Herodes interroget Scribas, dicens:

36

O vos Scribe; interrogati dicite si quid de hoc Puero scriptum videritis in libro.
Tunc Scribe duo revolvant librum, et tandem, inventa quasi prophetica, dicant:

37

Vidimus, Domine, in Prophetarum lineis, nasci Christum in Bethleem Jude, civitate David, Propheta

sic vaticinante.
Et ostendentes eum digito, Regi incredulo tradant librum.
Chorus:

38

⟨incipit⟩

Bethleem non es minima . . .
Tunc Herodes, visa prophetica, furore accensus, projiciat librum; ac filius eius,
audito tumultu, procedat pacificaturus patrem, et stans salutet eum:

39

Salve, pater inclyte; Salve, Rex egregie;

Qui ubique imperas. Sceptra tenens regia.

Herodes:

40

Fili amantissime, digne laudis munere;

Laudis pompam regie tuo gerens nomine.

Rex est natus fortior. Nobis et potentior.

Vereor ne solio Nos extrahet regio.

Tunc filius despective loquens de Christo offerat se ad vindictam dicens:

41 Contra illum regulum, contra natum parvulum,

Jube, pater, filium hoc inire prelium.

Tunc demum dimittat Herodes Magos, ut inquirant de Puero, et coram eia spondeat
regi nato, dicens:

42 Ite, et de Puero diligenter investigate,

et invento, redeuntes michi renunciate, ut et ego veniens adorem eum.

Magis egredientibus, precedat stella eos, que nondum in conspectu Herodis apparuit.
Quam ipsi sibi mutuo ostendentes, procedant. Qua visa, Herodes et filius minentur
cum gladiis.
Magi:

43 Ecce Stella in Oriente previsa

iterum precedit nos lucida.

Interim Pastores redeuntes a presepe, veniant gaudentes et cantantes in eundo:

44 O regem celi... ⟨incipit⟩

Ad quos Magi:

45 Quem vidistis?

Pastores:

46 Secundum quod dictum est nobis ab Angelo de Puero isto, invenimus infantem pannis

(♭)

involutum et positum in presepio in medio duum animalium.

Postea Pastoribus abeuntibus, Magi procedant post stellam usque ad precepe
cantantes:

47 Quem non prevalent propria magnitudine

Celum, terra atque maria lata capere,

(♭)

De virgineo natus utero ponitur in presepio.

Sermo cecinit quem vatidicus stant simul bos et asinus.

Sed oritur stella lucida, praebitum Domino obsequia.

Quem Balaam ex Judaica nasciturum dixerat prosapia.

Hec nostrorum oculos fulguranti lumine prestrinxit lucida,

Et nos ipsos provide ducens ad cunabula resplendens fulgida.

Tunc Obstetrices, videntes Magos alloquantur:

48 Qui sunt hii qui, stella duce, nos adeuntes inaudita ferunt?

Magi:

49 Nos sumus quos cernitis, reges Tharsis et Arabum et Saba dona ferentes Christo nato, Regi, Domino,

quem stella ducente, adorare venimus.

Obstetrices ostendentes Puerum:

50

Ecce puer adest quem queritis. Jam properate et adorate, quia ipse est redemptio mundi.

Magi:

51

Salve, Rex seculorum!   Salve, Deus deorum!   Salve, salus

mortuorum!

Tunc procidentes Magi adorent Puerum et offerent.

52 Primus dicat:

Suscipe, Rex, aurum, Regis signum.

Secundus:

Suscipe mirrham, signum sepulture.

Tertius:

Suscipe thus, tu vere Deus.

Istis factis, Magi incipiant dormire ibi ante presepe, donec Angelus desuper apparens,
moneat in sompnis ut redeant in regionem suam per aliam viam. Angelus dicat:

53

Impleta sunt omnia que prophetice scripta sunt. Ite, viam remeantes aliam, nec delatores

tanti regis puniendi eritis.

Magi evigilantes:

54

Deo gracias. Surgamus ergo, visione moniti angelica, et, calle mutato, lateant Herodem

que vidimus de Puero.

Tunc Magi abeuntes per aliam viam, non vidente Herode, cantent:

55

⟨incipit⟩

O, admirabile commercium; creator generis . . .

Tunc venientes in choro dicentes:

56

Gaudete fratres, Christus nobis natus est; Deus homo factus est.

Tunc Cantor incipit.

56a

Te Deum   Sic finit.

⟨ II   THE SLAYING OF THE CHILDREN⟩

⟨A⟩d interfectionem Puerorem induantur Innocentes stolis albis, et gaudentes
per monasterium, orent Deum dicentes:

⟨O⟩ quam gloriosum   est regnum . . .

Tunc Agnus ex inproviso veniens, portans crucem, antecedat eos huc et illuc, et
ille sequentes cantent:

Emitte agnum,   Domine . . .

Interim Armiger quidam offerat Herodi sedenti sceptrum suum, dicens:

Super   solium   David . . .

Interea Angelus super Presepe apparens moneat Joseph fugere in Egiptum cum
Maria. Angelus dicat tribus vicibus *Joseph*:

Joseph, Joseph, Joseph, fili David!

Postea dicat hec:

Tolle   puerum et matrem eius, et vade in   Egiptum,   et esto   ibi   usque dum dicam tibi.

Futurum est   enim   ut   Herodes   querat   puerum ad perdendum   eum.

92

Joseph abiens, non vidente Herode, cum Maria portante Puerum, dicens:

6 〈incipit〉

Egipte, noli flere . . .

Interim Armiger, nuncians Magos per aliam viam redisse salutat prius Regem; postea dicat:

7 Rex, in eternum vive! Delusus es, Domine; Magi viam redierunt aliam!

Tunc Herodes, quasi corruptus, arrepto gladio, paret seipsum occidere: sed prohibeature tandem a suis et pacificetur, dicens:

8 Incendium meum ruina restinguam.

Interea Innocentes, adhuc gradientes post Agnum, decantent:

9 Agno sacrato pro nobis mortificato,

Offerimus Christo sub signo luminis isto.

Agno salvemur, cum Christo conmoriemur.

Splendorem patris splendorem virginitatis,

Multis ira modis ut quos inquirit Herodis

Armiger suggerat Herodi dicens:

10 Discerne, Domine, vindicare iram tuam,

Forte inter oculos occidetur et Christus.

Et stricto mucrone jube occidi pueros;

Herodes tradens ei gladium dicens:

11 Armiger eximie, pueros fac ense perire.

Interim, occisoribus venientibus, subtrahatur agnus elam, quem abeuntem salutant Innocentes:

12 Salve, Agnus Dei! Salve, qui tollis peccata mundi, alleluia!

Tunc Matres occidentes orent occisos:

13 Oremus, tenere natorum parcite vite.

Postea, jacentibus Infantibus, Angelus ab excelso ut moneant eos, dicens:

14 Vos qui in pulvere estis, expergiscimini et clamate.

Infantes jacentes:

15 Quare, non defendis

sanguinem nostrum, Deus noster?

Angelus:

16 Adhuc sustinete modicum tempus, donec impleatur numerus fratrum

vestrorum.

Tunc inducatur Rachel, et due Consolatrices; et stans super Pueros plangat, cadens
aliquando, dicens:

17 Heu! teneri partus, laceros quos cernimus artus!

Heu! dulces nati, sola rabie jugulati!

Heu! quem nec pietas nec vestra coercuit etas!

Heu! matres misere, quae cogimur ista videre!

Heu! quid nunc agimus cur non hec facta subimus!

Heu! quia memores nostroque levare dolores.

Gaudia non possunt, nam dulcia pignora desunt!
Consolatrices excipientes eam cadentem dicentes:

18 Noli, virgo Rachel, noli dulcissima mater,

Pro nece parvorum fletus retinere dolorum.

Si que tristaris, exulta que lacrimaris.

Namque tui nati vivunt super astra beati.

Item Rachel dolens:

19 Heu! Heu! Heu! Quomodo gaudebo; dum mortua membra videbo;

Dum sic commota fuero per viscera tota?

Me facient vere pueri sine fine dolere.

O dolor! O patrum! mutataque gaudia matrum

Ad lugubres luctus! Lacrimarum fundite fletus,

Judee florem patrie lacrimando dolorem!

Item Consolatrices:

20 Quid tu, virgo, mater Rachel, plorans formosa, cuius vultus Jacob delectat?

Ceu sororis agnicule lippitudo eum juvat!

Terge, mater, flentes oculos. Quam te decent genarum rivuli?
Item Rachel:

21 Heu, heu, heu! Quid

me incusastis fletus incassum fudisse, Cum sim orbata nato, paupertatem meam (qui solus) curaret;   qui   non

hostibus   cederet   angustos terminos, quos michi Jacob adquisivit, Quique stolidis fratribus, quos multos, proh

dolor, extulit, esset profuturus?

Tunc Consolatrices, esupinantes Infantes, dicentes:

22 Numquid flendus   est   iste, qui regnum   possidet   celeste,   Quidque prece   frequentu   miseris

fratribus apud Deum   auxilietur?

Item Rachel cadens super Pueros:

23 Anxiatus est in me spiritus meus; in me turbatum est cor meum.

Tunc Consolatrices abducant Rachel, et Angelus interim de supernis dicat antiphonam
que sequitur:

24 ⟨incipit⟩

Sinite parvulos . . .

Ad vocem angeli surgentes Pueri intrent chorum dicentes:

25

O Christe, quantum patri exercitum juvenis, doctus ad bella maxima; populis predicans, colligis,

umbras suggens cum tantum miseris.

Dum hec fiunt, tollatur Herodes et substituatur in loco eius Filius eius, Archelaus,
et exaltetur in regem. Interim Angelus ammoneat Joseph in Egiptum, quo prius
secessit, dicens:

26

Joseph, Joseph, Joseph, fili David! Revertere

in terram Judam; defuncti sunt enim qui querebant animam pueri.

Tunc Joseph revertatur cum Maria et Puero, secedens in partes Galilee dicens:

27 ⟨incipit⟩

Gaude, gaude, gaude, Maria Virgo; cunctas hereses . . .

Cantor incipit:

27a

Te Deum laudamus . . .

Sic finit.

Notes on the Literal Transcription

⟨THE REPRESENTATION OF HEROD⟩

1 The settings of these Gospel texts seem to be
2 non-liturgical. In No. 1 the manuscript has
"natus est *nobis*" instead of the "vobis" of the
Vulgate text.

3 This is an ancient Christmas antiphon-setting
of the Gospel words.

4 This is a borrowing of the trope of the Introit
5 of the (3rd) Christmas Mass. It is a curious fact
6 that Fleury uses for the first two words ("Quem
quaeritis") not the usual music of the trope
but that of the Easter "Quem quaeritis . . ." In
the acting-version I have, in No. 6, inserted the
word "hic" between "Adest" and "parvulus."
It is found in all other versions that use the
item. I have also put in a clef change that had
been overlooked.

11 Regarding the threefold "Ecce Stella," I must
confess some doubt as to the actual pitch of the
music of the last repetition. If the F clef as written in the manuscript is really intended to be
placed in the top *space* of the clef (a position
that I have not met with before) then the music
as I have given it must for that single phrase be
read as being a tone lower. If the clef is meant
for the top *line* (again most unusual) then the
phrase should be a minor third lower than what
I have given, and thus repeating the First King's
phrase an octave lower.

8 - I have already commented on Fleury's fine and
42 individual use of certain "pool" items in the
Court scene, as well as there being a good deal
(THE of music that appears to be Fleury's own. In the
COURT cases of the two lyrical items (Nos. 15 and 39-
SCENE) 41), the settings of which in my opinion belong
to the first and second rhythmic modes respectively, it will be noted that the scribe has actually defined the endings of the lines of the poetry
by means of stops. But not consistently. In No.
40 an extra note (an A) seems to have crept in
at the word "digne." I believe that the scribe
lost count for the moment of his repeated "A's."
I cannot credit that the extra A was intended as
a *pressus*.

In No. 38 only the beginning of a setting of St.
Matthew II, 6 is given—a so-called *incipit*. I
have completed text and music from the version
found in Madrid, MS 289, fol. 109v.

44 This *incipit* is the beginning of an ancient antiphon, no longer in the Roman liturgy. I have
completed it in the acting-version with the kind
assistance of the Benedictines of Solesmes. In
the Fleury MS. the neumes for the second syllable of "celi" are ambiguous.

46 This reply of the Shepherds is a good example
of Fleury's originality, both text and florid free-
rhythm setting. They quote to the Magi of the

Angel's first address to them as well as some snatches of his music.

47 This splendid setting of the major part of the text of a liturgical sequence seems to adapt itself to the first rhythmic mode. As I have previously mentioned, the music is not that of the original sequence and may well be Fleury's own. I have, in the acting version (6th line), preferred "praebitura" to "praebitum," adding another C to the melody, as in the line which follows, and which has the same music.

55 This *incipit* belongs to a liturgical antiphon. This time it can easily be completed, since it is still used in the Roman liturgy.

48
ONWARD In the Magi's oblation scene and the closing stages there is a good deal of use of "pool" material, but with the usual Fleury individuality in regard to melody.

⟨THE SLAYING OF THE CHILDREN⟩

1 This *incipit,* belonging to a liturgical antiphon of Vespers, I have completed from the modern *Antiphonale Romanum.*

2 This *incipit,* belonging to a liturgical antiphon of Lauds, is no longer in the Roman liturgy. I completed it from the Sarum Antiphonal.

3 This *incipit,* belonging to a liturgical antiphon of Lauds, I have completed from the modern *Antiphonale Romanum.*

6 This *incipit,* belonging to a Matins Responsory no longer extant, I have completed from the Sarum Antiphonal. The verse which follows is from Hartker.

9 Although the scribe wrote the rhyming stanza "Agno sacrato . . ." in continuous prose fashion he indicated the line-endings by means of stops and capitals. The music falls readily into the first rhythmic mode.

10 In the third line *oculos* is assumed to be a scribal error for *occisos.* In the matter of textual corrections one can rely on the previous *literary* editing by Karl Young, Du Méril, and others.

14
(RUBRIC) *Ut moneant* is assumed to be a scribal error for *admoneat.* Incidentally, small errors such as case endings (e.g. *vultum* for *vultus*) have been corrected in the transcription without comment.

17
ONWARD In the long lyrical rhyming scene between Rachel and her Consolers the scribe has again indicated the line-endings of the poetry by means of stops and capitals. The setting is clearly in regular trochaic (first mode) rhythm.

18 It has already been remarked that the Notker sequence text which here commences is not given the original sequence music, but a setting (continued from No. 17) that must surely be Fleury's own.

20 Textual scribal errors have been corrected in the acting-version to *ploras, annicule,* and *lippitudo* respectively.

21 In the setting of this portion of the Notker text there are two notes (a *clivis*) which seem to be going spare. Also, by comparison with other versions of the text, Fleury appears to have left out two words—"qui solus" (three syllables) between "meam" and "curaret." In the acting-version I have inserted them and compromised on their setting. The liquescent of "an*gus*tos" might perhaps be A,B, instead of B,C.

24 I completed this *incipit,* which belongs to an antiphon no longer extant, from Hartker, through the help given me by Solesmes.

27 The text of this *incipit* seems to belong to an antiphon (no longer extant) for the Assumption. But the music is not the same, and none of the Gregorian scholars whom I consulted (even those of Solesmes) could identify it. Finally, Noah Greenberg supplied a version of his own, which kept to the mode and the style of the *incipit.*

W. L. SMOLDON

Date Due